TIME AND TIDE

RUSKIN STUDIES
1996

Time & Tide

RUSKIN AND SCIENCE

Edited by

MICHAEL WHEELER

*Professor of English Literature
and Director of the Ruskin Programme
Lancaster University*

PILKINGTON PRESS LTD
LONDON

FIRST PUBLISHED 1996
BY PILKINGTON PRESS LTD
YELVERTOFT MANOR
NORTHAMPTONSHIRE NN6 7LF

ISBN 1 899044 10 2

PRODUCED, DESIGNED AND TYPESET BY:
A.H. JOLLY (EDITORIAL) LTD
YELVERTOFT MANOR
NORTHAMPTONSHIRE NN6 7LF

PRINTED IN GREAT BRITAIN

CONTENTS

List of Plates
7

Note on Contributors
9

Editor's Preface
11

1 *Ruskin To-day*
James S. Dearden
15

2 *'Paradise Lost': Ruskin and Science*
Robert Hewison
29

3 *'The Eagle and the Whale?': Ruskin's argument with John Tyndall*
Francis O'Gorman
45

4 *'Over yonder are the Andes': Reading Ruskin reading Humboldt*
Paul Wilson
65

5 *Was Ruskin a Materialist?*
Clive Wilmer
85

6 *'Job's Iron Pen': Ruskin's use of engraved illustration in* Modern Painters
Alan Davis
98

Ruskin Bibliography 1986–1995
David Barron
119

LIST OF ILLUSTRATIONS

1   Ryuzo Mikimoto who established the great Ruskin Collection in Japan. (*page 17*)

2   Ryuzo Mikimoto sitting with Arthur Severn in Ruskin's bedroom at Brantwood during one of his visits to Coniston. (*page 17*)

3   Plate 11 from William Blake's series of engraved illustrations of the book of Job (1826). (*page 103*)

4   *The Last Furrow*: facsimile from *Ariadne Florentina* of the wood engraving after Holbein. (*page 105*)

5   Enlarged foreground detail from the engraving by J.T. Willmore (1828) after Turner's *Richmond*. (*page 111*)

6   Engraving by J.T. Willmore (1828) after Turner's *Richmond*. (*page 111*)

7   Enlarged foreground detail from the etching by J.C. Armytage after Turner's *Richmond*, from *Modern Painters* V. (*page 113*)

8   Engraving by J.C. Armytage illustrating the foreground of Turner's *Richmond* to a high degree of finish, from *Modern Painters* V. (*page 113*)

9   Engraving by J. Cousen after Turner's *Goldau*, from *Modern Painters* IV. (*page 116*)

EDITORIAL ADVISORY BOARD

NOTES ON CONTRIBUTORS

David Barron is Subject Librarian for English Literature and a number of other Humanities subjects at Lancaster University Library. He collaborated with Keith Hanley on the *Annotated Critical Bibliography of William Wordsworth* (Prentice Hall Harvester, 1995), and prepared the entry on Ruskin for the forthcoming third edition of the Cambridge Bibliography of English Literature.

Alan Davis's research interests are interdisciplinary. He has published papers on the design of prehistoric rock carvings (a topic not wholly unrelated to his paper in the present volume), and he collects nineteenth-century etchings, engravings and drawings. His current ongoing investigation of Ruskin as a printmaker is the outcome of an amateur interest in Ruskin's work of more than twenty years' standing. He teaches physics at Lancaster Royal Grammer School.

James S. Dearden has served as Curator of the Ruskin Galleries at Bembridge and Brantwood since 1957. He is a Companion of the Guild of St George, Secretary of the Ruskin Association, and Joint General Editor of the Whitehouse Edition of Ruskin. He has written and edited numerous books and articles on Ruskin and allied subjects.

Robert Hewison published *John Ruskin: the Argument of the Eye* in 1976. He subsequently curated the exhibition *Ruskin and Venice* at the J.B. Speed Art Museum, Louisville, Kentucky in 1978; edited *New Approaches to Ruskin: Thirteen Essays* in 1981; and published an edition of the *Catalogue of the Rudimentary Series* of the Ruskin Art Collection at Oxford in 1984. His most recent work in the field of Ruskin studies is *Ruskin and Oxford: The Art of Education*, the catalogue of an exhibition he curated at the Ashmolean Museum, Oxford in 1996. Since 1981 he has written on the arts for the *Sunday Times*, and in 1995 he became Professor of Literary and Cultural Studies at Lancaster University.

Francis O'Gorman read English at Lady Margaret Hall, Oxford (1986–89) before writing a doctoral thesis there on Ruskin's late science. In 1993 he became Lecturer in English Literature at Pembroke College, Oxford, and in 1996 he takes up the post of Senior Lecturer in English at Westminster College, Oxford. His publications include work on Ruskin and W. B. Yeats.

Clive Wilmer is a poet and literary critic who has edited the Penguin Classics Edition of *Unto This Last and Other Writings* by John Ruskin. His most recent book is *Selected Poems* (Carcanet Press, 1995).

Paul Wilson is a lecturer in English and Communication Studies at Nelson and Colne College of Further Education. His MA dissertation examined the interplay of science and myth in *The Queen of the Air*. He is currently completing his PhD thesis at Lancaster University on Ruskin's geological writings.

ABBREVIATIONS

References to Ruskin's published works are taken from *The Works of John Ruskin*, Library Edition, edited by E.T. Cook and Alexander Wedderburn, 39 vols (London: Allen; New York: Longmans, Green, 1903–12), unless otherwise stated, and are indicated by volume and page numbers in the text, thus: 24.301–2. References to *The Diaries of John Ruskin*, ed. Joan Evans and John Howard Whitehouse, 3 vols (Oxford: Clarendon, 1956–59) are indicated in the text, thus: *D*, 432.

PREFACE

Time & Tide offers the reader some of the latest and liveliest work on John Ruskin – Victorian Britain's greatest critic of art and architecture, its most astringent and often idiosyncratic social commentator, a wonderfully observant artist, an inspired teacher, geologist, naturalist, collector, and prophet – together with a large bibliography listing recent scholarship. Ruskin's ideas influenced many aspects of the cultural and intellectual life of Britain and America in the nineteenth century, and had a shaping effect on the work of figures as various as Gandhi, Tolstoy and Proust. The recent revival of interest in his work reflects the fact that his most original statements – on environmental themes, the relationship between ethics and aesthetics, social welfare, architecture and tradition – speak to our generation as well as to his own.

The volume takes its name from one of Ruskin's own publications – *Time and Tide, by Weare and Tyne: Twenty-Five Letters to a Working Man of Sunderland on the Laws of Work*. These letters were addressed to Mr Thomas Dixon, a working corkcutter, during the agitation for reform in the spring of 1867, and first appeared in newspapers.

The multidisciplinary Ruskin Programme at Lancaster University is the centre for Ruskin studies, and exists to carry out research on Ruskin, to publish its findings, and to promote exhibitions, conferences and courses on his work. Since 1990 the Ruskin Programme has held over 100 research seminars. These are weekly meetings attended regularly by about 20 people: senior scholars from a number of disciplines in the Humanities, research students, and others (not all of them members of the University) who are interested in Ruskin, with visitors from other institutions in Britain and overseas – over 40 of whom have delivered papers.

The essays in *Time & Tide* began life either as papers delivered to the Ruskin Programme's research seminar, or as the Programme's annual public lecture, addressed to a wider audience. The seminar hears papers of two kinds: those related to its current research project – in the academic years 1993/94–1995/ 96 the project was 'Ruskin and Aesthetics: Modern Painters, 1843–1993' – and those, generally by visiting speakers, on other Ruskin topics. The plan is for at least half the essays in any one annual issue of *Time & Tide* to have a common theme, thus giving coherence and permanent value to each volume, while at the same time allowing for variety of subject and treatment in the remaining essays. In this inaugural year the subject is 'Ruskin and Science'. Those outside the university world who fear that Ruskin and all he represents can somehow be diminished by academic treatment will, I hope, find the discussions of this theme both accessible and engaging, and will come to share the view that Ruskin is, first and last, an intellectual, and one who deserves careful and extensive study.

Before introducing the essays on science, however, a word about the first essay, entitled 'Ruskin To-day', and the Mikimoto Memorial Ruskin Lecture (1995) on which it is based. The Ruskin Library of Tokyo, which promotes Ruskin studies and houses the Mikimoto collection of Ruskin material, generously contributed to the Ruskin Programme's research in recognition of the Programme's parallel relationship to the Whitehouse Ruskin Collection which is shortly to be housed in the Ruskin Library at Lancaster. Although we had mounted an annual public lecture at Lancaster since 1991, it was felt that the natural choice of speaker for the inaugural Mikimoto Memorial lecture was James S. Dearden, who is retiring as Curator of the Ruskin Galleries, Bembridge School, and Brantwood in 1996 after almost forty years of exceptional service to Ruskin studies. In surveying the whole world of Ruskin – literally as well as metaphorically – 'To-day', Dearden draws upon his uniquely detailed knowledge of Ruskin drawings, biography and bibliography, and of a wide range of collections in Britain, the USA and Japan. The reader may care to turn to the Dearden entries in the 'Ruskin Bibliography 1986–1995' at the end of this volume in order to get some sense of the contribution he has made to Ruskin scholarship. I trust he will continue to contribute for many years to come.

A second annual Ruskin Lecture (1994), also aimed at a non-specialist 'town-and-gown' audience, follows Jim Dearden's. Robert Hewison, now Professor of Literary and Cultural Studies at Lancaster University, is one of the most prolific and engaging writers of the succeeding generation of Ruskin scholars, many of whom carried out their postgraduate research at Oxford and were helped and supported by Dearden when they visited the Ruskin Galleries at Bembridge. Hewison wrote his lecture entitled '"Paradise lost": Ruskin and Science' when he was planning his exhibition on 'Ruskin and Oxford: The Art of Education', mounted at the Ashmolean Museum, Oxford, and the Ruskin Gallery, Sheffield in 1996 and the subject of a handsome catalogue published by the Clarendon Press. So the lecture has a strongly Oxonian emphasis, moving from the undergraduate years and Ruskin's encounter with the clerical scientists who taught him, through the planning and building of the Oxford Museum with his old friend Henry Acland, into the post-Darwinian world in which Ruskin fiercely opposed what he called the 'scientific people', and eventually the resignation of his Oxford chair for the second time, ostensibly on anti-vivisectionist grounds.

In a wide-ranging review of an important but somewhat neglected aspect of Ruskin, Hewison does not have the space to discuss particular aspects of the theme in detail. This is the task of two younger scholars, and here it is worth noting that Francis O' Gorman, working in Oxford, and Paul Wilson, writing his doctoral thesis at Lancaster, like their contemporaries such as Caroline Blyth (Oxford) and David James (London), can cite a wealth of scholarly material by literary scholars who write on Victorian science – including Gillian Beer, Tess Cosslett and Kate Flint – but few who focus upon Ruskin. O'Gorman discusses Ruskin's argument with John Tyndall over glaciation, demonstrating that this was indeed 'a crucial intersection in Victorian culture'. While Ruskin protested against what he perceived to be a changing intellectual climate which threatened certainty itself, he was also – paradoxically and thus, for him, typically – drawn to the very language of flux and inconstancy associated with the new science. Two of Ruskin's great themes – authority and facts – emerge as central to his argument with Tyndall, as indeed they were to his argument with the whole modern world in which he found himself.

Paul Wilson's emphasis is upon influence rather than opposition: he argues that, whereas the influence of de Saussure on Ruskin has frequently been noted, the influence of Humboldt has been ignored. Ruskin can be located among those younger scientists of the 1830s whose agenda was shaped by Humboldt: hence his recording the intensity of the blue of the sky on his cyanometer, his calculating the amount of debris brought down from the mountains by a typical Alpine stream, and his measurement of the angles of the summit of the Matterhorn. Yet, under pressure from friends – largely on religious grounds – Ruskin sought to distance himself from the Humboldtian tradition, denying influence as he did in other cases, most famously that of Pugin.

After these two detailed analyses of Ruskin's relationship to individual scientists, Clive Wilmer offers more general reflection which deliberately eschews contextualization in the nineteenth century. In answer to his own question, 'Was Ruskin a materialist?', Wilmer concludes that he was not, in either the vulgar or the philosophical sense of the word, but that he was unable or unwilling to distinguish between a truth and the material that embodied it; and that he remained essentially Christian, while citing Plato more than any other philosopher. More specific perceptions are also offered by Wilmer, including the suggestion that Ruskin's rejection of Constable and some of the Dutch landscape painters was grounded in his belief that they were materialists.

Alan Davis's essay strikes out in a quite different direction by examining Ruskin's use of engraved illustration in *Modern Painters*. Many of these illustrations, Davis argues, represent Ruskin's attempt to extend the capabilities of engraving as an interpretative medium, and an analysis of them can help us to understand *Modern Painters*, and indeed Ruskin himself. Following a brief reminder of the history of engraving in the early nineteenth century, the essay considers Ruskin's concept of engraving, and his movement towards a symbolic understanding of the engraver as a ploughman, in a tradition coming down from Dürer and Blake. Interestingly, Ruskin's views on engraving were forward-looking in a number of respects.

Time & Tide also seeks to keep the reader abreast of recent developments in Ruskin studies by providing a bibliography – here a listing of the enormous amount of work published in the past ten years, and in future an annual bibliography of Ruskin studies. As well as a number of major new scholarly monographs on Ruskin and a whole host of articles in journals and chapters in books, the number of doctoral theses listed, particularly from the USA, is notably high, indicating that a younger generation of scholars has been actively engaged in Ruskin studies in the 1980s and early 1990s. Outside Britain and the USA, the increasing interest in Ruskin in Japan is noteworthy, as is the smaller but significant growth in Ruskin studies in Germany. Work in Italy has been stimulated by Jeanne Clegg and Paul Tucker, through the research associated with their exhibition on 'Ruskin and Tuscany'. It is hoped that the Ruskin Programme's next project, on '"A Perpetual Paradise": Ruskin's Northern France', will stimulate further work from French scholars who become involved in our research.

The inauguration of *Time & Tide* coincides with the final stages of the construction of the new Ruskin Library at Lancaster University, to which the Whitehouse Ruskin Collection will be moved from the Isle of Wight this coming winter in readiness for the official opening next summer. The Ruskin Foundation is responsible for both the Collection and Brantwood, where the remainder of the Collection will continue to be on display on a rotation basis. In future years, then, *Time & Tide* can also provide a forum for some of the scholarly work emanating from the Ruskin Library, and with this in mind there will be space in the next issue for 'Notes', or shorter pieces, as well as full-length essays.

M.D.W.
Lancaster
June 1996

14

I

Ruskin To-day

The 1995 Mikimoto Memorial Ruskin Lecture,
Lancaster University, 24 October 1995

JAMES S. DEARDEN

JOHN RUSKIN's father was an industrious man. John James Ruskin began work at the age of 16; worked for nine years without a holiday; paid off the debts of £1,192 8s 11d which his father had left; married; bought a house, and by 1835 he employed five servants and valued his entire property at £39,246 14s 11d. By now he considered that he had reached the stage of respectability at which he should become armigerous. Many years later, in his autobiography, *Præterita*, John Ruskin described how he and his father went to the College of Heralds. They consulted with the heralds, paid their £5 10s 6d, and received a grant entitling them to bear arms, with a crest of a boar's head, selected 'as reasonably proud, without claim to be patrician' (35.390). For their motto they selected the Latin 'Age quod agis' – Do what you do. Later, Ruskin tells us, he changed the motto on his own seal into 'To-day', 'tacitly underlining to myself with the warning "The night cometh, when no man can work"'.

'Ruskin To-day' is such an obvious title for a book that I felt sure that several people would have already used it. However, on checking, I find that only Kenneth Clark's excellent volume of Ruskin selections bears the title. The newest organization within the Ruskin world – the Ruskin Foundation – has recently adopted Ruskin's arms and his motto, 'To-day', and thus it seemed appropriate at this, the first of the new series of annual Mikimoto Memorial Ruskin Lectures, that I should look at the state of the Ruskin world to-day.

I should like to say at the outset, how pleased and honoured I feel at being invited to deliver this lecture. I suppose I am the one person who for many years has been in touch with almost all of the people and organisations in the world with an interest in Ruskin. For example, I was first in touch with Mr and Mrs

Mikimoto and Mrs Homma, the son and daughter of Ryuzo Mikimoto, about a couple of years after their father's death in 1971.

Ryuzo Mikimoto was one of the small group of great Ruskin collectors who worked dedicatedly in the early years of this century to build up their collections – people like the engineer, Haddon C. Adams, the carpenter, F. J. Sharp, and the politician and educator, J. Howard Whitehouse. Strangely, although they were collecting at the same time, they did not then know each other.

Ryuzo Mikimoto (PLATE 1) was born in 1893. His father, Kokichi Mikimoto, had worked for many years to grow and successfully develop and market the cultured pearl. Ryuzo Mikimoto entered the Imperial University of Kyoto and here it was that he was introduced to the writings of John Ruskin. Ruskin himself had first been introduced to the Japanese public by a translation of Mrs Ward's *Prophets of the Nineteenth Century*, in 1903.

Mikimoto was captivated by Ruskin's thoughts on culture, and he devoted his life to studying Ruskin and his ideas, and to collecting his books, manuscripts, letters and drawings. He travelled to England and met Arthur Severn either at his London house or at Brantwood, in 1919, and in five other years up to 1930. On one of these occasions he was photographed with Arthur Severn in Ruskin's bedroom at Brantwood (PLATE 2). From Arthur Severn and others he was able to buy Ruskin letters and drawings, and he quickly built up an important collection. He established the Ruskin Society of Tokyo in 1931, and was the editor and chief writer of its more-or-less monthly *Journal*, which was published until 1937. Mikimoto's first publication on Ruskin appeared in 1922, and in addition to his work on the *Journal*, in the next 42 years he was to write or translate a further 42 books by or about Ruskin.

In 1934 Ryuzo Mikimoto opened the Ruskin Library in Tokyo. This became the centre for those in Japan between the wars who were interested in Ruskin. On the ground floor there was a hand-made crafts shop, with a tea room on the second floor. Regular meetings and celebrations were held. In addition to publishing his books, Mr Mikimoto fostered the arts and crafts by commissioning young sculptors to create original works. He had a series of beaten copper panels made, embossed with one of Ruskin's portraits of Rose La Touche. He had another sculptor create a statue of Ruskin, based on the Millais Glenfinlas portrait of 1853. A third created a new bronze head and shoulders, based on the 1890s full-length statue of Ruskin by Gutzon Borglum.

During the war the Mikimoto collection was stored for safety at Shima, the seaside town where the Mikimoto pearl farms were. Meanwhile, since Mr Mikimoto devoted his life to Ruskin, his son and daughter had to take respon-

PLATE 1 (*left*): Ryuzo Mikimoto who established the great Ruskin Collection in Japan.

PLATE 2 (*below*): Ryuzo Mikimoto sitting with Arthur Severn in Ruskin's bedroom at Brantwood during one of his visits to Coniston.

sibility for the family business. Thus, as I remember them telling me, Ruskin was not their favourite person. It was not until after the death of their father in 1971 that Yoshitaki Mikimoto and his sister Mrs Homma 'discovered' Ruskin for themselves in clearing up their father's estate. In turn, they have now opened a new Ruskin Library, where the books and other artefacts of their father's collection are now available to scholars. Many of the manuscripts and drawings in the collection are housed for safety from both theft and earthquake in a vault on the seventh floor below ground in one of the city's main banks, where my wife and I had the pleasure of examining them two years ago.

The foundations of the great American collections had already been laid by the time that Ryuzo Mikimoto discovered Ruskin. Unlike the other American millionaire collectors of the turn of the century who made their money out of oil, transport, and other such activities, the Morgans were an old-established family, and their wealth came from banking. Pierpont Morgan's collection began with autographs, and it was not until the death of his father – also a collector – in 1890 that Morgan began to collect in earnest. He collected on a princely scale. Morgan's tastes were for the autograph manuscripts of great authors, the finest medieval manuscripts, the most important incunabula, and fine bindings – a Gutenberg *Bible* on vellum, the 1459 Maintz *Psalter*, the only complete copy of Caxton's edition of Mallory's *Morte d'Arthur*, a tenth century *Gospels* written on purple vellum, the autograph manuscripts of Dickens's *Christmas Carol* and Keats's *Endymion*. Between 1900 and 1906 Morgan built a library in New York – a Renaissance building based on a Mantuan palace that has been called one of the seven wonders of the Edwardian world. The great chimney piece of the east room is the work of Ferro, the fifteenth-century Florentine sculptor, while the polychrome ceiling of the same room came from a cardinal's palace in Lucca.

By chance, both Ruskin and Morgan were keen collectors of Sir Walter Scott – and here is an interesting association. Ruskin's father bought the manuscript of *The Fortunes of Nigel* in 1831 and eventually Ruskin inherited it. Later, in the 1870s and early '80s Ruskin bought several more Scott manuscripts, and in February 1881 he told his bookseller that he was 'speechless with indignation since you let go that *Guy Mannering* manuscript'. The manuscript was, in fact, bought by Junius Morgan, and he gave it to his son Pierpont. In the 1890s, shortage of funds at Brantwood led to the sale of most of Ruskin's Scott manuscripts, and *The Black Dwarf*, *Peveril of the Peak* and *Woodstock* were in the Morgan Library by 1894. When Joan Severn consulted T. J. Wise about disposing of the *Fortunes of Nigel* manuscript in 1921, he was very pessimistic. The boom years were over, he said, and he thought the best price Joan could get would be £500 – a fair margin of profit since Ruskin's father had paid £25 for it. Eventually it was sold to Hugh Walpole for £400 and he later gave it to his old school, King's at Canterbury.

In England, George Allen, who was Ruskin's publisher from the early 1870s, had built up an enviable collection of Ruskin manuscripts. He had also been scrupulously careful to obtain documentary evidence from Ruskin that these manuscripts belonged to him. Very soon after Ruskin's death in 1900, plans began to be laid for the publication of the Ruskin *Library Edition*, the collected edition of his works, and a lot of scheming took place, to which I have referred elsewhere.[1] At about this time George Allen decided to part with his Ruskin manuscripts. The reason is not clear. He may have been selling them to raise money to finance the new edition, or more likely – in my opinion – to put the manuscripts firmly beyond the reach of Joan Severn, Ruskin's legatee, and Alexander Wedderburn, the clever King's Counsel, who was also one of Ruskin's literary executors. Whichever may have been the case, in the spring of 1902 Allen sent Pierpont Morgan a list of the Ruskin manuscripts which he was prepared to sell. The list included the manuscripts of the *Stones of Venice*, priced at £6,000, and *Modern Painters*, at £7,700, together with a dozen others. Morgan replied offering £5,000 for *Modern Painters*, and Allen accepted his offer. At first sight, £5,000 may not seem very much. But people who know about these things tell me there is a formula for updating 1902 prices to their present-day equivalent – and Morgan was effectively paying £450,000 for the manuscript, by to-day's standards.

Five years later, Allen re-offered some of the manuscripts to Morgan, and remembering how he had been beaten down £2,000 on his asking price for *Modern Painters*, he increased the price of *Stones of Venice* from £6,000 to £6,600. Again, Morgan couldn't resist an important autograph manuscript, and he offered £5,000, which Allen again accepted. At the modern equivalent of £900,000 for the two manuscripts, these are certainly the most expensive Ruskin manuscripts ever to change hands. With foundations like these, and your own bank behind you, it is not surprising that the Ruskin collection now in the Pierpont Library in New York is one of the most significant in the world.

The American William K. Bixby made his fortune out of railways. As a collector he was interested in a wide range of subjects. In fact his bookplate includes the image of an octopus sending its tentacles in every direction to collect

1 James S. Dearden, 'The Library Edition of the Works of John Ruskin', *Book Collector*, 44 (1995), 51–66.

material. In the early years of this century, Bixby bought from George Allen some of the manuscripts that hadn't interested Morgan – *The Seven Lamps of Architecture* and *Unto this Last*. Bixby's collection was always on the move, and he disposed of important parts of it in 1917 and '18. He had known Henry Huntington for some years, and had already sold items from his collection to Huntington. From Bixby's 1918 sale, Huntington bought the manuscripts of *Seven Lamps* and *Unto this Last*, together with a group of letters.

Henry Huntington made an immense fortune from the promotion of railways, and from many other activities in California. About 1908, at the age of around 58, he retired from business, and devoted the rest of his life to his library. In slightly under twenty years, his wholesale purchases of other libraries – he bought the E. Dwight Church library for one million dollars in 1911, 1600 lots at H. W. Poor's sale, significant lots at the Hoe sale, twenty-five Caxtons and the Kemble-Devonshire collection of plays from Chatsworth, and others – created a library that was worthy to stand with the national libraries of Europe. It is particularly strong in manuscripts and early printed books – Gutenberg *Bibles* and over 5,000 other incunabula, 300,000 rare books, 38,000 English books before 1700, and a staggering five million manuscripts.

Huntington had a few miscellaneous Ruskin letters in his library from its early years. However, the foundations of his Ruskin collection were really laid in 1918, with his purchases from Bixby. In retrospect, knowing how the American millionaire collectors of this period vied with each other, it is curious that Morgan didn't buy *Seven Lamps* and *Unto this Last* from George Allen – however, he didn't, and this lapse was Huntington's eventual gain. It was a few years later, in 1923, that Huntington bought his largest group of Ruskin letters – 526 letters written between 1873 and 1887 to his Coniston neighbour Susan Beever. Building on these foundations, in 1925 Huntington bought the manuscripts of *Lectures on Architecture and Painting*, *The Two Paths*, *Pre-Raphaelitism*, and *The Elements of Perspective*, from George Allen's son, William. The Huntington Library has continued to add various important groups of letters to its holdings.

The third of the great American collections is in the Beinecke Library at Yale University. This also began as a private collection, but more recently than those I have just described. As a Freshman at Yale, R. B. Adam was stirred to such enthusiasm by the study of Ruskin in his English course, that he determined to read his complete works. Whether or not Adam achieved his aim and read the whole of Ruskin isn't recorded. However, he developed into a dedicated book collector, and although he was principally known for his Johnson collection, he did assemble a remarkably complete collection of Ruskin's printed works. Adam aimed to collect every variant edition of the volumes issued during Ruskin's lifetime – and he was remarkably successful in his aim.

Having decided to concentrate his interests on the 18th century, in 1926 Adam sold part of his collection which did not fit into this category. At this time he had not decided to give his Ruskin material to Yale, and so his sale included a number of rarer Ruskin pieces, such as the first edition of *Salsette and Elephanta*, the Wise forgery of *Queen's Gardens*, a first edition of *Harbours of England*, and two copies of *Poems* 1850. One of these was the copy given by Ruskin's father to W. H. Harrison, Ruskin's 'first editor', who had collaborated in producing the edition. It was bought at Adam's sale by Jerome Kern. Adam's second copy must have been in the variant 'female' binding. Thus when Adam's Ruskin library was given to Yale in 1929 it lacked the thirty-eight manuscripts and printed pieces which had already been sold. But over the years these gaps have more than been made good, by both purchase and gift, especially from Charles Goodspeed and Chauncey B. Tinker.

The Beinecke's holding of Ruskin manuscripts began in earnest at the Ruskin sale at Sotheby's in 1930. The records seem to show that Yale was bidding in its own right, and bought several lots. They also bought, subsequently, a number of lots from Charles Goodspeed, the Boston bookseller and Ruskin collector, who was also buying at the sale. Their purchases, as a result of this sale, immediately made their holdings one of the principal ones. At this time they bought twelve volumes of Juvenilia, six volumes containing 1,600 letters from Ruskin to his father, one of the *Stones of Venice* notebooks, nine other miscellaneous notebooks, and the manuscripts of *King of the Golden River*, *Lectures on Art*, *Val d'Arno*, and other Oxford lectures, and *Proserpina*. Many other letters and manuscripts have been acquired subsequently, some by purchase, others by gift.

Also now at Yale are the six notebooks which comprise the manuscript of Ruskin's autobiography, *Præterita*. These were bought at the 1930 sale by Charles Goodspeed, and retained in his personal collection. Unhappily, in February 1941, there was a disastrous fire, and his home was burned down. Much was destroyed, but many important books and manuscripts were saved, including the *Præterita* manuscript, although some of the volumes are badly charred around the edges. In the following month Goodspeed gave the manuscript to Yale.

Of course, there are other Ruskin collections in America, most significantly at Princeton, where there is more Juvenilia, and the manuscripts of *Deucalion* and part of *Our Fathers have told us*. The collection at Harvard arrived there by a slightly different route from the other American collections. Charles Eliot Norton, a firm friend of Ruskin who became one of his executors, was Professor of Fine

Art at Harvard; Charles Herbert Moore, another friend of Ruskin's, was Norton's assistant and successor. Between them, Norton and Moore assembled some thirty drawings by Ruskin which they used in their teaching. These are now in Harvard's Fogg Art Museum, together with fifteen from Norton's own collection and other sources – over sixty in all – making probably America's largest single holding of Ruskin drawings. Additionally the library there has a substantial holding of Ruskin, Severn and Norton correspondence.

But America holds more than just Ruskin letters, drawings and manuscripts. Despite Ruskin's dislike of smoking, in America you can buy the 'Ruskin' cigar. The Ruskin Art Club is the oldest club in Los Angeles. And there are at least six towns called Ruskin in North America. Ruskin, Nebraska, got its name because the engineer building the Chicago, Kansas and Nebraska Railway was a student of English history, and he named the various halts after well-known English figures. Ruskin, Nebraska, was founded in 1887; it is twenty-five miles from the centre of America (however you establish that) and a few years ago, when I had a correspondent there, it had a population of some 200 people. Around are some of the biggest cereal farms in the country, and the town has its own newspaper, *The Ruskin Leader*. In fact, the whole place is a Ruskinomaniac's delight, with its Ruskin Feed and Grinding Service, Ruskin Grain Company, Ruskin Produce, Ruskin Service Station, and Ruskin Lions Club!

Ruskin, Tennessee, followed in 1894, and this really *was* a Ruskinian town. The founder of the community, and of the Ruskin Commonwealth, was an Indiana newspaper man called Charles Wayland. His periodical, *The Coming Nation*, sold internationally. It was planned that it would make enough profit to extend the colony which was established by Wayland in order to put into practice what he understood were Ruskin's ideas expressed in *Fors Clavigera*. It really was a practical American version of the Guild of St George. Workers in the community were paid in tokens redeemable at the Commonwealth Store, and by the late 1890s there were some 250 inhabitants living in seventy white-washed wooden houses grouped around the printing works. However, inevitably there were disagreements; the founder withdrew, and the Commonwealth collapsed. A few believers moved to Georgia where they founded another Ruskin. Ruskin, Tennessee, quickly became a ghost town, and Ruskin, Georgia, did not long survive.

Ruskin, Florida, is located on Tampa Bay. Dr George Miller founded a Christian Socialist college here in about 1908 and called it Ruskin College. He too admired Ruskin's ideals, and wrote :

Ruskin declares that moral character is impossible without manual labour, and Ruskin University believes it, not because Ruskin said it, but because experience proves it.[2]

Paul Dickman was a student at the college, and he later settled in Ruskin and developed the community as a centre of agriculture, and particularly of to-mato-growing. You have heard of 'The Big Apple' – well, Ruskin, Florida, for a number of years promoted itself as 'The Big Tomato', although it has recently changed its image to that of a beach, sailing and recreation centre. It appears to be a very flourishing town.

There are also Ruskins in Missouri, in Illinois, and we have recently found another in British Columbia, Canada. The Canadian Ruskin was founded in 1895 by an English settler called Whetham. He apparently was so impressed by Ruskin's ideas that he wanted to honour him in this way. Ruskin is a small community located on the banks of the Fraser River. There is a school, a com-munity hall built in 1922, and a settlement comprising a few wooden houses. The main industry is lumber.

But one must not be misled into thinking that all Ruskin is in America or Japan! London has its fair smattering of Ruskin Walks, Gardens, Roads, Streets, Closes and Avenues – remember that the Tax Man lives in Ruskin Avenue, Kew! A number of these streets, not unnaturally, are in south London, where Ruskin spent much of his life. John Ruskin Street was formerly called Beresford Street, and was re-named in honour of Ruskin because as a small boy he attended the Beresford Street Chapel. The building is still there today, in a rather derelict state.

Ruskin Walk leads off Herne Hill, almost opposing the site of the Ruskin house at No 28. In the distance you can see the spire of St Paul's Church. In here is a memorial to Ruskin which incorporates all of the types of marble found in St Mark's, Venice – but not as successfully. A little further north, down the hill, a whole housing estate occupies the site of the family's next home at 143 Denmark Hill, although across the road is Ruskin Park. A little way along the road from Camberwell Green is St Giles Church, where Ruskin and his friend, Edmund Oldfield, were responsible for the design of part of the east window, and not far away, in Grove Lane, is Camberwell Hall, now a private house. It was here that Ruskin lectured in 1865 to the Camberwell Working Men's Institute on 'Work and Play', the lecture that was to form the first chapter of his *Crown of Wild Olive*.

2 George McA. Miller 'Academic Center', *The Arena*, 29 (July 1903), 607–8, cited in unpublished thesis, Carrie Lynn Kastner, '"Utopia on the Half-Shell": a story of how Ruskin, Florida,
   acclimatized to its Land and its Inventors', 1986, p. 14.

Of course Ruskin was not confined to London. At Oxford he was an under-graduate at Christ Church. They gave him rooms at Corpus when he became the first Slade Professor of Fine Art. While occupying this chair, Ruskin founded the Ruskin Drawing School and endowed a Drawing Mastership. The present Drawing Master is Stephen Farthing. While Slade Professor, Ruskin gave the Drawing School a teaching collection comprising many of his own drawings; these are now in the Ashmolean Museum. He had already given the university a collection of some fifty Turner watercolours (and so that they wouldn't feel offended he gave Cambridge a collection of twenty-five Turners at the same time). The Ashmolean's Western Art Library also houses the important collection of Ruskin's published works which Cook and Wedderburn assembled while they were editing the *Library Edition*, but curiously the transcripts of the original material which they made at this time are in the Bodleian Library. The Bodleian also has a collection of Ruskin letters, notably those to his lifelong friend, Henry Acland.

Also in Oxford is Ruskin College. The connection here is one of Ruskin's teaching. Ruskin always advocated the education of the working man. Ruskin College was originally established to run short-term residential courses for just this purpose, and was named in honour of Ruskin's aims.

Further north, the Ruskin Gallery in Sheffield is in the city centre, just twenty yards across the pedestrian precinct from the Crucible Theatre. Three or four years ago this area was to have been named Ruskin Square, in honour of Ruskin's benefactions to the city – but at the eleventh hour the good burghers of Sheffield heard of a politically incorrect alliance of Ruskin's in the 1860s, and instead the area was named Tudor Square. Apparently Henry Tudor was thought more politically acceptable than John Ruskin! The collection in the Ruskin Gallery here was returned to Sheffield ten years ago when the present gallery was opened. The collection is the property of the Guild of St George. The Guild was established by Ruskin in the 1870s in an attempt to combat the social injustices of the day. It was a grandiose scheme, and only partially successful, although it still flourishes today. The Guild fosters and helps various schemes of which we think Ruskin would approve if he were alive today. It owns farms and woodland in the Wyre Forest, known as Ruskinland, part of a beautiful Hertfordshire village, and one of its principal assets is its collection which Ruskin placed in Sheffield in the last century, in an attempt to bring to the people of the city examples of great art and architecture and beauty. The collection contains a number of Ruskin's own drawings, but its principal strength lies in works by young artists commissioned by Ruskin, made to record important buildings and to study great paintings. Here too are books and minerals and architectural casts, and a magnificent collection of medieval manuscripts. In addition to its permanent display the Ruskin Gallery in Sheffield holds temporary exhibitions, lectures and many other activities which makes it a very thriving organisation.

One of the world's great libraries, the John Rylands Library in Manchester (now part of Manchester University) has an important collection of Ruskin papers, principally strong in letters relating to the Guild of St George, and given to the library by the widow of Canon Rawnsley, one of the three founders of the National Trust. Until relatively recently the Trust ignored the fact that Ruskin had said in *Fors Clavigera* that we should have a national store instead of a national debt (27.14), and a non-state body to care for interesting and beautiful places. Hardwick Rawnsley, who came under Ruskin's influence as an undergraduate at Oxford, and Octavia Hill, who had managed the London property which Ruskin inherited from his father, and where he had put into practice his theories of fair rents and security of tenure, went on to put Ruskin's ideas into practice when they became two of the founders of the National Trust.

Mention of the National Trust naturally leads me to the Lake District, where the Trust is the largest landowner. But its first property was the small plot, very much smaller than this room, where the Ruskin Memorial was raised on Friar's Crag on Derwentwater in 1901. On one side of this monolith is incised the quotation from Ruskin's *Deucalion* :

> The Spirit of God is around you in the air that you breathe, – His glory in the light that you see; and in the fruitfulness of the earth, and the joy of its creatures; He has written for you, day by day, His revelation, as He has granted you, day by day, your daily bread. (cf. 26.266)

Indeed, the spirit of Ruskin is around you too. Friar's Crag was one of the first places he remembered as a small boy, and on one of his earliest visits to the Lakes he also went to Coniston. A few years later he was to draw Coniston Old Man from the eastern shore of the lake and to use it as an illustration in his first important publication, *The Poetry of Architecture*. Forty years later he was to buy Brantwood from where he had drawn the Old Man, and make it his home for the rest of his life. In 1900 Ruskin died and was buried in Coniston churchyard. Brantwood and its contents were inherited by Joan and Arthur Severn who had lived with him for thirty years and more. Later the house and many of the contents were bought by John Howard Whitehouse.

Howard Whitehouse had discovered Ruskin at about the same time as the American millionaire collectors. With infinitely smaller resources and with half a century's dedication he was to build what is now the world's leading Ruskin collection, which not only contains a huge quantity of material, but which also contains Brantwood itself. When Whitehouse first discovered Ruskin, as a young man in the 1890s, he founded the Ruskin Society of Birmingham, in an attempt to bring the Ruskin message to the people of his home town. At this time Whitehouse was working in the offices of Cadbury Brothers at Bournville, where he was instrumental in persuading them to start their pensions scheme. He founded their boys' club, with its own magazine, *Cameraderie*, which grew into the Works Magazine, just as its library grew into the Works Library. Whitehouse went on to become the first secretary of the Carnegie Dunfermline Trust. From there he went to Toynbee Hall in east London as secretary, when William Beveridge, later to become the architect of the Welfare State, was Sub-Warden. Then for a while Whitehouse ran the university settlement at Ancoats in Manchester before entering Parliament in 1910 as the Liberal member for Mid-Lanark. In Parliament he prospered; he was Parliamentary private secretary to Charles Masterman at the Home Office when Churchill was Home Secretary, and later to Lloyd George when he was Chancellor. But during the war, Whitehouse, who saw conscription as an infringement of personal liberty, joined the group of MPs who opposed Lloyd George's introduction of this measure. Of course he ruined a very promising political career; in the re-arrangement of constituencies which took place at the end of the war, Mid-Lanark disappeared, Whitehouse lost his seat – and went on to found a boarding school for boys at Bembridge in the Isle of Wight, in order to put to the test some of his own and some of Ruskin's educational theories. And all the time he was collecting Ruskin books, letters, manuscripts and drawings.

By the late 1920s his collection had grown to such a size that it was necessary for him to extend his home by adding the two Ruskin Galleries to house everything. And just in time. At the series of sales in 1930 and 1931 which dispersed the contents of Brantwood, Whitehouse was one of the principal buyers. At this time he added many thousands of letters to his collection, noticably a large number of family letters, and the 3,000-odd letters from Ruskin to his cousin Joan Severn. Several hundred books from Ruskin's library came to the collection at this time, together with the manuscripts of several books, the twenty-eight volumes of Ruskin's diaries, a mass of working papers for *Stones of Venice*, a large number of drawings by Ruskin and his associates – and Brantwood itself. Whitehouse continued to collect almost up to the time of his death in 1955. Since then, the late Lord Lloyd of Kilgerran, his executor, and subsequently the Hon. Mrs Robins and their families, have done their utmost to secure the future of the whole collection.

The collection has been expanded whenever possible, principally by gifts. Importantly, the bequest of the Haddon C. Adams collection, which I mentioned earlier, brought many books and drawings to Bembridge. Adams had bought extensively, but selectively, from Brantwood before the sales. At the sales he made a few more purchases, and his collection contained particularly significant pieces, such as the watercolour by Ruskin's father which used to hang above his son's bedroom mantlepiece.

The picture which used to hang below it, a still life of fruit by W. H. Hunt, used to belong to F. J. Sharp, a teacher of carpentry in Barrow. He had also been an ardent Ruskinian for many years, and he too spent his life collecting.[3] With the very modest means at his disposal, he too bought material from the sales, and subsequently from dealers. While his collection was never as big as the other major collections, it contained many items of the greatest importance. Following Sharp's death in 1957, his collection was split up. Principally it found its way to America, and ultimately to the Morgan Library, but I was able to obtain quite a lot of material for Brantwood and Bembridge.

It is not possible to fit the whole of Ruskin – even just 'Ruskin to-day' into one lecture. Time does not allow me to tell you about the opera *Modern Painters*, recently staged in America at the Santa Fe Opera House, or the play commissioned by the National Trust and staged at the Richmond Theatre in Yorkshire – still less of past theatrical performances – *The Bride of Denmark Hill*, *Ordeal by Marriage*, and *The Ruskin Mélange*. No more have I time to tell you of the Ruskin Museum at Coniston, the collection of his drawings in the Abbot Hall Gallery in Kendal, or the Ruskin Cabinet at Whitelands College in Putney, and of the Ruskin-inspired May Queen Ceremony which still continues there annually, because I have to look forward to Ruskin tomorrow.

For many years there have been more books on the market about Ruskin than *by* him. This situation is being rectified. In Germany a series of translations of Ruskin's books is beginning publication. In this country, the new Whitehouse Edition of Ruskin aims to put his principal texts back into print. Modern technology makes it possible for the thirty-nine volumes of the Ruskin *Library Edition* to be put onto one CD-ROM disk which is being published by Cambridge University Press for the Ruskin Foundation in the autumn of 1996, a year which also sees an important exhibition in Oxford and Sheffield illustrating Ruskin's association with that university whilst also looking at his methods as a teacher. Calling itself 'Ruskin 2000', a great assemblage of those interested in Ruskin

3 For further information *see* Van Akin Burd, 'Frederick James Sharp, 1880–1957: Portrait of a Bibliophile, xxxli', *Book Collector*, 44 (1995), 542–73.

met recently in London to help co-ordinate the exhibitions and other activities which are planned already for the year 2000, to mark the centenary of Ruskin's death.

But the greatest of all of the future activities is the building of the Ruskin Library here at Lancaster University, and the moving to it from Bembridge of the great Whitehouse Ruskin Collection. This will at the same time put it nearer to the other part of the collection at Brantwood, enable it to be used by a greater number of people, and facilitate its greater conservation and care.

Ruskin, after all, is not new to Lancaster. He often stopped at the Kings Arms during his travels; the Mayor of Lancaster proposed the vote of thanks at the ceremony at Coniston in 1934 when Brantwood was opened to the public, and he 'voiced appreciation of so excellent a national memorial'.[4] And I am sure there must be those of you who see him almost daily – looking out from one of the bronze panels on the Queen Victoria monument in Dalton Square. Ruskin is already here with us to-day, almost wherever we look.

4   *Lancashire Daily Post*, 23 April 1934.

2

'Paradise lost'

Ruskin and Science

The 1994 Ruskin Lecture
Lancaster University, 26 October 1994

ROBERT HEWISON

IT IS ALWAYS a great pleasure to be asked to talk about Ruskin, but it is a special pleasure to be asked to talk about him in Lancaster. Lancaster is close to the Lake District, and in getting closer to the Lake District, we are getting closer to Ruskin. For much of his life the Lakes were a kind of spiritual home for Ruskin, and Brantwood, the house looking across Coniston Water to the Old Man of Coniston, was his physical home from 1872 until his death in 1900.

When Ruskin gave a lecture in Kendal in October 1877 he said something similar about his pleasure in being close to the Lakes:

> I knew mountains long before I knew pictures; and these mountains of yours, before any other mountains. From this town of Kendal, I went out, a child, to the first joyful excursions among the Cumberland lakes, which formed my love of landscape and of painting: and now, being an old man, I find myself more and more glad to return. (26.243)

Ruskin, born in London in 1819 and therefore only 58 when he made this claim to great age, belonged to the first of several generations to have their perceptions of nature – as represented at its most magnificent and awe-inspiring by the Lake District – shaped by their reading of the English Romantic poets, most especially Wordsworth and Coleridge, and by looking at the English landscape painters of the early nineteenth century, of whom Turner was the most prominent. They came to this part of the world in order to give themselves up to the direct experience of the place itself – mediated as that experience was by the romantic expectations raised by their reading and their enjoyment of contemporary art. Ruskin, who said that one of his earliest memories was of a visit to Friar's Crag above Derwentwater at the age of five-and-a-half, in 1824, was eager from the start to translate these experiences into both drawings and verse. In 1830, at the age of eleven, following what was already his fourth visit to the Lakes, he produced a 2,510-line verse account of his and his parents' summer tour. He called it *Iteriad*, meaning 'excursion', and not only was it modelled on Wordsworth's *Excursion*, it included a mention of seeing Wordsworth himself:

> ... old Mr Wordsworth at chapel of Rydal
> Whom we had the honour of seeing, beside all.[1]

The poetry may not be up to Wordsworth's standards, being more like bad Byron, but not every eleven-year-old turns out 2,500 lines of rhyming verse.

Yet what was Ruskin doing, besides soaking up the sights as an early customer of the tourist industry? He was writing, he was drawing, but, as his own verse records, he was also *looking*, and in a very special way. He describes himself:

> Now surveying a streamlet, now mineralizing, –
> Now admiring the mountains, and now botanizing, – [2]

It turns out that Ruskin's interest in the Lakes was more than sentimental: it was scientific. In a very real sense the Lakes were not just Ruskin's open air studio – they were also his laboratory.

In the late twentieth century we have become so used to thinking in terms of an absolute division between the arts and the sciences that it is difficult to imagine a time when their relationship was not one of mutual incomprehension or even downright hostility. The division has been built into our educational system and embedded in our culture. But at the beginning of the nineteenth century the relationship was far from antithetical. As Tess Cosslett has pointed out, then, scientific investigators shared their sense of spiritual and ethical values with the literary writers, and the writers in turn, as she puts it, assimilated 'the values and the world view of the prevailing scientific culture'.[3]

The harmony between art and science was easier to sustain because that scientific culture was in its methodology much closer to that of the painters and poets, in that it was principally one of observation and classification. The early

---

1 John Ruskin, *Iteriad; or, Three Weeks Among the Lakes*, ed. J. S. Dearden (Newcastle upon Tyne: Graham, 1969), p. 113 (lines 615–16).

2 Ibid., p. 37 (lines 359–60).

3 Tess Cosslett, *The 'Scientific Movement' and Victorian Literature* (Sussex: Harvester, 1982), p. 3.

nineteenth-century scientist observed and recorded the phenomena of the natural world, like a painter, and, like a poet, named them. There were mathematicians, chemists and physicists, but the leading scientific disciplines of the day depended upon observation: astronomy, geology, mineralogy, botany. Science was concerned with gaining empirical knowledge of the natural world – and the scientist was called a 'natural philosopher'. The scientist and the artist shared a moral commitment to accurately recording the truth of their perceptions. It is worth reminding ourselves that we are talking of a period before the invention of photography: the observer had to rely on the accuracy of his own eye and of his own verbal or visual description, not that of a camera.

Ruskin, a gifted draughtsman from an early age, shared the scientists' moral commitment, and he shared their intellectual discipline. Among the earliest surviving drawings by Ruskin are a series of maps made when he was eight; there can be no more literal way of expressing the features of the earth than to present them as a map. As his father, John James Ruskin, whose wealth freed Ruskin to follow his interests wherever they took him, proudly remarked: 'From boyhood my son has been an artist, but he has been a geologist from infancy.'[4] As Ruskin reminded his audience in Kendal in 1877, a passion for geology preceded his passion for art, and remained with him throughout his life. His collection of minerals at Brantwood was to grow to more than 3,000 specimens. His first published prose, at the age of fifteen, was an article in *The Magazine of Natural History* in 1834, titled 'Enquiries on the Cause of the Colour of the Water of the Rhone' – a scientific as well as a painterly question.

Truth to nature was one of Ruskin's by-words. Consider for instance this passage:

> A long-experienced eye can, at a glance from the summit of a mountain, point out with considerable certainty the different formations of which a country is composed. Landscape-painters, by confounding together all these differences, or by combining them irregularly, fail not only in accuracy, but in giving their work that appearance, which shows, at first glance, that it is not only a copy of nature, but a copy by one who has formed a distinct conception of the general and particular features of the inequalities observable on the surface of the earth.[5]

That is not, as it happens, from Ruskin, but from Robert Jameson's 1821 *Manual of Mineralogy*, which he owned as a boy. Ruskin was to make such an argument for accurate observation one of the foundation stones of his defence of Turner

4   Quoted in E. T. Cook, *The Life of John Ruskin* (London: Allen, 1911), I, 32.
5   Robert Jameson, *Manual of Mineralogy* (Edinburgh: n.p., 1821), pp. 363–64.

as the greatest of modern painters. It was Turner's superior powers of observation – judged by the yardstick of Ruskin's own scientific knowledge – that led Ruskin to say that Turner 'is as much of a geologist as he is of a painter' (3.429).

Ruskin's scientific enthusiasms continued in parallel with his aesthetic training. In 1837 he joined the London Geological Society, becoming a Fellow in 1840. At his first meeting he heard a paper by Charles Darwin, lately returned from the expedition to South America and the Galapagos Islands that supplied the evidence for the theory that was to prove so devastating to Ruskin's worldview when it was finally published twenty years later. When Ruskin went up to Christ Church, Oxford in that same year he immediately began to attend the lectures on geology given by one of the more eccentric fellows of his own college, the Reverend William Buckland, who in 1819 had become the University's first Professor of Geology. Buckland's house was crammed with specimens – alive as well as dead, for he kept a small menagerie of animals, including a bear and a jackal. Buckland also had a penchant for serving his dinner guests dishes of crocodile, or mice baked in batter. Ruskin wrote to his father: 'I attended Dr Bucklands lectures, very delightful – kept us laughing all the while – saw some splendid specimens. He is evidently a very talented man'.[6] Ruskin was later invited to dinner – it is not known what was on the menu – and had a long discussion with another guest, Darwin – though like the menu, the contents of the discussion are not recorded. Buckland drew on Ruskin's talents as a draughtsman to prepare illustrations for his lectures – and it is worth noting that Ruskin's own techniques as a lecturer, for which he was to become famous, were in the tradition of the scientific lecture with its demonstration of specimens.

There is no doubt that the observational science of the early nineteenth century helped to shape Ruskin's artistic practice. For one thing, it encouraged him to give up any thoughts of being a poet. Ruskin published a number of poems in his teens, and after much labour succeeded in winning the Newdigate Prize for poetry at Oxford in 1839, but he gradually became disenchanted with an imaginative process that appeared to lead away from the externally observed, towards the internal emotions of the writer. On the other hand, Ruskin's vision was not that of the cold Cartesian eye that gazed out on the world in order to control it. Though he abandoned poetry, Ruskin evolved a passionate descriptive prose that sought accurately to render the facts of the natural world, but

---

6 John Ruskin, letter of 8 February 1837, in *The Ruskin Family Letters: The Correspondence of John James Ruskin, His Wife, and Their Son, John, 1801–1843*, ed. Van Akin Burd (Ithaca: Cornell University Press, 1973), II, 429.

which at the same time truthfully recorded the writer's response. The act of description is also an act of the imagination, but it is one where the emotion comes from the object to the viewer, and not the other way round. To project one's emotions onto the external world, Ruskin argued, was a pathetic fallacy, substituting the subjective for the objective. It was not wrong – indeed it was much to be desired – to have an emotional response to the natural world, but that emotion could only be genuine if it encouraged, and did not hinder, a complete encounter with the object. It was the genius of Turner to perceive the natural facts of the world, and then raise them onto a higher plane through his imaginative response.

So far I have been trying to demonstrate the harmony that existed between the arts and sciences at the period of Ruskin's intellectual formation. Essentially, the artist and scientist shared a common subject, the natural world; they understood that world in a common way. Even more significant than the lack of conflict between the arts and sciences at this time was the lack of conflict between science and religion. The early nineteenth century was the heyday of Natural Theology, epitomized by the Reverend William Paley's book of that name, published in 1802. The argument was that everything in nature had been created by God for a purpose, and that science helped to show this. The so-called 'design argument' treated God as the master architect and craftsman. It was consistent that many of the early naturalists should also be clergymen: the Church could provide a living for an intellectual of scientific bent, while in the case of Oxford and Cambridge, at this period it was a necessary qualification for a full fellowship at a college to be in holy orders.

The Reverend William Buckland is a case in point. He had used the arguments of natural theology to persuade Oxford to accept geology as a legitimate subject. In 1836 Buckland had published *Geology and Mineralogy Considered with Reference to Natural Theology*, one of the so-called Bridgewater Treatises sponsored by the eighth Earl of Bridgewater to demonstrate the goodness of God in the field of astronomy, physics, geology and animal, vegetable and human physiology. 'No reasonable man', wrote Buckland, 'can doubt that all the phenomena of the natural world derive their origin from God; and no one who believes the Bible to be the word of God, has cause to fear any discrepancy between this, his word, and the results of any discoveries respecting the nature of his works'.[7]

---

7   William Buckland, *Geology and Mineralogy Considered with Reference to Natural Theology* (London: Pickering, 1836), I, 9.

To a strict Evangelical Protestant like Ruskin, these were comforting words at a period when the literal interpretation of the book of Genesis was coming under critical attack. Science reinforced his love of nature, and therefore of God, while the typological interpretations of the Bible that he heard every Sunday from Evangelical pulpits encouraged him to treat the world as another version of the book of God. The process whereby accurate, objective perception led to a higher, spiritual reading of the natural facts encouraged Ruskin to think in terms of what he called 'a science of the aspects of things'. In the third volume of *Modern Painters*, published in 1856, in a chapter significantly entitled 'The Moral of Landscape', he sought to redistribute the emphasis in the Aristotelian distinction between appearance and essence:

> We cannot fathom the mystery of a single flower, nor is it intended that we should; but that the pursuit of science should constantly be stayed by the love of beauty, and accuracy of knowledge by tenderness of emotion. Not is it even just to speak of the love of beauty as in all respects unscientific; for there is a science of the aspects of things, as well as of their nature; and it is as much a fact to be noted in their constitution, that they produce such and such an effect upon the eye or heart … as that they are made up of certain atoms or vibrations of matter. (5.387)

Ruskin's attitude to the science of his day – at least during the first half of the nineteenth century – explains how he came to be closely involved in one of the major academic controversies of the 1850s, one which happily was resolved in favour of Ruskin and the modernisers: the building of the Oxford Museum.

Ruskin had a personal as well as intellectual commitment to the project, in that its protagonist was one of his closest friends from undergraduate days at Christ Church, Henry Wentworth Acland. In spite of the presence of figures like Buckland, Oxford in the 1830s and 1840s was in general even less scientifically minded that it had been in the late seventeenth century when the first ever public museum, the Ashmolean, was built to house the natural history collections of the Tradescants and of the antiquarian Elias Ashmole. The principal subjects for undergraduate study were Classics, Mathematics, Ancient History and Theology. Acland, however, had gone on from the conventional grounding in classics and mathematics to qualify, by studying in London and Edinburgh, as a doctor. A combination of circumstances brought him back to Oxford in 1845 when he accepted the post of Lee's Reader in Anatomy, an appointment attached not to the University as such, but to Christ Church. In 1846 he took up a medical practice in the town. Acland was a good doctor, but he was also a consummate academic politician, and he was determined that science should find its proper place in the university curriculum.

To that end he campaigned both for the teaching of natural philosophy, chemistry and physiology as part of the standard pass and honours courses, and for the building of a new museum to house the various collections of specimens that had been accumulated by the University's scientific pioneers. For Acland, the physical sciences were 'facts connected, illuminated, interpreted, so as to become the intelligible embodied expression to His creatures of the Will of a God', a view with which Ruskin did not quarrel.[8] Just as Acland threw in a complimentary mention of Ruskin's *Modern Painters* into his pamphlet calling for proper attention to the natural sciences, Ruskin complained in the *The Stones of Venice* that Oxford, and European education generally, 'despises Natural History' (11.258).

Acland was to have his way, and the University reforms of the 1850s meant that a new school of Natural Science was established, but there was a major battle over the new museum. Although the building was – and now very much is – a museum, it would be much better to think of it as functioning as a science park. (Over time the area around the museum has become the University's science area.) Under one roof were to be studied Astronomy, Geometry, Experimental Physics, Chemistry, Mineralogy, Geology, Zoology, Anatomy, Physiology and Medicine. Each discipline had its own work-rooms, laboratories, lecture-rooms, and studies, grouped round three sides of a covered court, where the specimens relating to each discipline could be displayed. The University's science library – for which Acland in his role as Radcliffe Librarian was responsible – was to be rehoused on the first floor.

That the design finally chosen for this new building was one of the first examples of the Gothic Revival should not obscure the radical modernity of the project. In the battle of the styles that had preceded the choice of the Dublin architect Benjamin Woodward's Gothic design, it was argued that Gothic was far more adaptable then the Palladian alternative. To model the chemistry labs on the medieval kitchens at Glastonbury was not an eccentricity. The potentially explosive experiments of the chemistry department called for a high degree of ventilation, in a structure semi-detached from the main building.

As Acland himself recorded, the object of the museum 'and the method of

---

8 Henry Wentworth Acland, *Remarks on The Extension of Education at the University of Oxford in a letter to the Rev. W. Jacobson D.D., Regius Professor of Divinity, and Canon of Ch.Ch,, Oxford* (Oxford: Parker, 1848), p. 12.

carrying it out, were then violently opposed in the University'.[9] While the main spokesman of Oxford's theological party, Dr Pusey, voted for the scheme – and indeed gave two guineas towards the cost of embellishments – the Vice-Chancellor at the start of the campaign, the Reverend Plumptre 'gave as the reason of his opposition that Science tends to Infidelity' (16.235). A more widely held objection was the sheer cost of the project – though here too there were theological objections, since the money was expected to come from the substantial profits that had been made by the Clarendon Press from printing the Bible. Finally in 1854 the University Convocation narrowly voted for the scheme to go ahead, on a budget of £30,000. It was enough to build the building, but it wasn't enough to finish it as its champions would have liked.

The question of the decoration of the Oxford Museum is important, not only because of Ruskin's close interest in the scheme as the first fruits of his arguments for the revival not just of Gothic design, but of Gothic work practices, as argued for in *The Seven Lamps of Architecture* and *The Stones of Venice*. The ruling idea of the decoration, both the interior, with its technologically advanced iron columns holding up the glass courtyard roof, and the exterior, was to make it a narrative expression of the contents of the building. Buckland's successor as Professor of Geology, John Phillips, was brought in to devise a scheme by which each shaft of the columns around the central hall was an example of a different British marble, while the capitals and bases were to be decorated with plants and animals arranged in their natural orders. As Phillips explained: 'we have always *desired* to employ so much of system as to make these ornamental parts of the fabric *really* and *obviously useful*, as part of the exhibition of natural objects.'[10] All this, Phillips wrote, was an expression, 'in rough stone', of the way in which 'the GREAT ARTIFICER moulds the lilies of the field and the leaves of the forest'.[11] The Oxford Museum, Gothic in spirit, designed to embody the principles of a harmonious classification of the natural order created by 'the great artificer', was a physical embodiment of the synthesis of art, science and religious belief at the heart of Natural Theology.

It is all the more ironic, then, that in 1860, with the building completed, but not yet equipped for use, the Oxford Museum should be the site of a famous con-

9 As part of the campaign to raise funds, Acland and Ruskin jointly published a short book, *The Oxford Museum* (London: Smith, Elder; Oxford: Parker, 1859), which went through five editions in slightly different formats. For the last edition (London: Allen, 1893), Acland added new material, quoted here, and reprinted at (16.235).

10 John Phillips, writing in Acland and Ruskin (1859), p. 94.

11 Ibid., p. 101.

frontation that blighted the paradisical garden of Natural Theology for ever. Once T. H. Huxley and Bishop Wilberforce had had their debate on Darwin's *On the Origin of Species*, science and religion began seriously to part company. Emblematically, Acland and Ruskin's scheme of decoration for the Oxford Museum has never been completed.

The fact was that as the century had progressed the benign world of Natural Theology had darkened, as the combined researches of astronomers, geologists, paleontologists and evolutionary biologists began to redraw the picture of Creation, while at the same time biblical scholars began to interpret the story of Genesis in such a way as to bring into doubt not only the authority of the text, but of the supposed author of that text. This was extremely damaging to popular belief, and to the security of mind of those like Ruskin who had to admit that the evidence produced by their observations pointed away from the account with which they had been brought up. Natural theologians like Buckland had tried to adjust the story to the facts, by arguing that the now accepted great geological age of the earth proved only that it had existed for aeons *before* God created man, or by suggesting that the 'days' of the Biblical account were in fact vast epochs of time. But the position became less and less tenable as knowledge grew. It is no wonder that Ruskin should write to Acland in 1851: 'If only the Geologists would let me alone, I could do very well, but those dreadful Hammers! I hear the clink of them at the end of every cadence of the Bible verses' (36.115). This was written eight years before Darwin published his theory of evolution, and it is fair to say that Ruskin experienced his crisis of faith – and lost his Evangelical certainty in the process – independently of Darwin's arguments. That did not, however, stop Darwin becoming the butt of many Ruskinian sarcasms in the years ahead.

What is striking about Darwin's theory of evolution, published as *On the Origin of Species by Natural Selection* in 1859, is that while it does indeed contradict the Mosaic account, it is nonetheless significantly organic, finding in the Universe (whose actual creator is not brought into the question) a higher harmony that expresses a natural law, underlining the kinship of man with nature. Darwin offered the organic metaphor of the tree, with divergent lines of speciation, and each new fork in each new branch dependent on the branching fork that had preceded it, with dead branches for the species which the paleontologists had shown to have existed, but which had since disappeared. The problem with this account, however, with its emphasis on the contingencies of environment as a major factor in the survival by adaptation of a species, was that it was no longer possible to present this process as a grand design, a mechanism, however intricate and subtle, whose outcome had been preordained by God. This, rather than the common parentage of men and monkeys, was destructive of previous confident certainties.

I have already mentioned the debate at the 1860 meeting of the British Assocation for the Advancement of Science between Darwin's advocate, T. H. Huxley, and Bishop Wilberforce, held before an excited crowd of clerics, scientists and young ladies in the empty library of the Oxford Museum. The location does add a dramatic irony to the story, but the truth is that the debate has acquired a retrospective significance that it was not perceived to have at the time – there are, for instance, very few contemporary accounts of the debate, while the subsequent history has been written from the point of view of the Darwinians. A more significant event in 1860 for intellectuals such as Ruskin was the publication of *Essays and Reviews*, seven essays, six of them by Anglican clerics, which sought to come to terms with the new Biblical criticism that substituted a historical approach for the traditional view of scripture as an inspired text. The seventh contributor to *Essays and Reviews*, however, was a geologist, Charles Goodwin, who demolished the Natural Theologians. According to Goodwin: 'the interpretation proposed by Buckland to be given to the Mosaic description will not bear a moment's discussion.'[12]

Whatever the immediate impact of the Oxford Museum debate, it does mark a paradigm shift, as the division between science and religion widened. Huxley's aggressive attitude towards clericalism, which he called 'the deadly enemy of science', was partly the product of wanting to establish science as an independent profession, in which amateur clerics, pottering around in Oxfordshire quarries, had no part.[13] But it is also true that the nature of science was changing: instead of proceeding from the gathering and classification of empirical data – what one might call a visible science – there was a shift towards the construction of technical hypotheses and deduction – the wave theory of light or the kinetic theory of gases – that were concerned with the invisible forces at work in the universe.

Ruskin – though he continued to meet Darwin from time to time – never came to terms with the theory of evolution. As Dinah Birch has written: 'The idea of incessant flux in Darwin's research on evolution was incompatible with

12 Charles Goodwin, 'On the Mosaic Cosmogeny', reprinted from *Essays and Reviews* (1860) in *Science and Religion in the Nineteenth Century*, ed. Tess Cosslett (Cambridge: Cambridge University Press, 1984), p. 128.

13 Thomas Henry Huxley in his *Autobiography*, quoted in Cosslett (1984), p. 1.

Ruskin's paramount belief that the physical world expressed moral and spiritual precepts that were irreducible and utterly unchanging.'[14] Ruskin, who almost certainly lived and died a virgin, had difficulty with the Darwinian emphasis on successful reproduction as the key to the survival of a species. For the evolutionary botanist, the purpose of a plant was to produce a seed; for the visually sensitized Ruskin, it was to produce a flower. Yet it is significant that Ruskin never really confronted the theory of evolution as such, while he was constantly referring to it obliquely and comically. The editors of the Library Edition of Ruskin's works tend to play down Ruskin's hostility to Darwin, but we should note this apparently eye-witness account of one of Ruskin's lectures at Oxford, when he had become the first Slade Professor of Art:

> It was at the Taylor Institution; a lecture on I forget which subject. Something brought up Evolution. Now, if there was one thing that roused his anger, it was Evolution: and so he abandoned his subject, notes, professorial style; a new light of scorn and wrath gleamed, and he went like a terrier at the obnoxious theory. Amusement filled those who knew his ways; amazement those who did not. It was such a meaningless theory, he said, it could only be understood by an example. Far off in the aeons (I quote from recollection) there was a hairbrush ...[15]

And according to the narrator, G. W. Kitchin, Ruskin went on to explain how a hairbrush, spinning in rotation with the earth, turned into a swallow. The lecture Kitchin describes was in fact the first of a series on ornithology that Ruskin gave at Oxford in 1873, although a published text did not appear until 1881. There Ruskin's satirical Darwinian example is recognizable, though somewhat different. If you were to fasten a hairbrush to a millwheel, Ruskin wrote, one that was

> within continual hearing of a steam-whistle, after a certain number of revolutions the hairbrush will fall in love with the whistle; they will marry, lay an egg, and the produce will be a nightingale. (25.36)

The example is if anything even more absurd – and what it does betray is precisely a fear of the consequences of reproductive processes.

Essentially, however, the difference between Ruskin and Darwin was that their theories were now operating on completely different planes. While Darwin found it simpler to leave the question of first causes out of the equation, for Ruskin, the issue was not what, on the evolutionary scale, people had been, or

14 Dinah Birch, 'Ruskin and the Science of *Proserpina*', in *New Approaches to Ruskin: Thirteen Essays*, ed. Robert Hewison (London: Routledge, Paul, 1981), p. 152.

15 G. W. Kitchin, *Ruskin in Oxford, and Other Studies* (London: Murray, 1904), p. 41.

what they might become; it was what they *were* that mattered. His objection to what he called 'the scientific mind' was its apparent unawareness of the moral choice between the forces of Life – Ruskin's ruling emblem of the Good – and Death – Ruskin's emblem for Evil. It was he said: 'the failure of the sense of beauty in form, and loss of faith in heroism of conduct, which have become the curses of recent science, art, and policy' (20.267).

Ruskin by no means abandoned science; indeed he gave more, rather than less attention to it in the latter part of his life. In the 1860s he continued his studies in geology – the science, as it happens, least affected by Darwinism – and published learned articles on the Alps in the *Geological Magazine* and the *Geologist*, taking part in the active debate about their formation. He sided with James Forbes on the subject of glaciers against John Tyndall, whose co-author in an attack on Forbes was Darwin's promoter, T. H. Huxley. He continued to acquire, catalogue and give away mineralogical specimens until the end of his active life, and in the 1870s he set out to compose what he called 'three grammars – of geology, botany, and zoology' (28.647).

These 'grammars', which appeared intermittently and in separate parts, were intended to serve both what he hoped would be the educational purposes of his utopian society, the Guild of St George, and to gather together his scientific commentaries at Oxford, where he taught as Professor of Art from 1870 to 1877, and from 1883 to 1885, and elsewhere. *Love's Meinie*, on birds, appeared between 1873 and 1881, *Deucalion*, on geology, between 1875 and 1883, and *Proserpina*, principally concerned with flowers, between 1875 and 1886. None was ever completed, and none, at a first reading, would appear to make very much sense.

Yet these extraordinary publications are the summation of Ruskin's 'science of the aspect of things'. They are about the description, the classification, and above all the *naming*, of things according to principles that are entirely Ruskin's own, but which are intended to put back what the scientists of his day appeared to be leaving out. Ruskin insisted on calling scientists, or at least the ideas espoused by the followers of scientists 'half-witted, because never entertained by any person possessing imaginative power' (26.336). As Dinah Birch has commented: in this context '"imaginative power" constitutes the missing half of Darwin's capacity'.[16]

For Ruskin, 'imaginative power' was the power of myth, the unifying, harmonizing system of ideas, images and values which synthesized all the disparate creative activities of mankind, from architecture to zoology, from engineer-

16 Birch, p. 153.

ing to economics. It had its roots in the founding Hellenic and Judeao-Christian myths of European literature, but it also carried a heavy freight of personal symbolism, as Ruskin increasingly found a means of sublimating his private agonies through the creative play of devising ever new systems of classification, and discovering ever more complex cross-references and cultural allusions. In his introduction to *Deucalion* he explicitly elevated myth over

> ... the Darwinian Theory. And in general, the reader may take it for a first principle, both in science and literature, that the feeblest myth is better than the strongest theory: the one recording a natural impression on the imaginations of great men, and of unpretending multitudes; the other, an unnatural exertion of the wits of little men, and half-wits of impertinent multitudes. (26.99)

There is not space here to explore the intricacies and reticulations of Ruskin's mythopoeic reclassification of the natural world. Fundamentally it is structured around those two all-powerful countervailing emblems alluded to earlier, Life and Death: Life representing the values of the science of aspects, Death the values of Darwinian theory. Tragically, the universal and the personal resonances of these myths sounded together in one last battle between Ruskin and the authorities at Oxford, and this time he was on the losing side.

As Ruskin grew older, he began to show an increasing horror of anatomy. Although he had once criticized Wordsworth because 'he could not understand that to break a rock with a hammer in search of crystal may sometimes be an act not disgraceful to human nature, and that to dissect a flower may sometimes be as proper as to dream over it', analytical science had got out of hand (5.359). The necessary association with death in anatomical study is consistent with Ruskin's mythopoeic arguments, but there may also be an element of sexual fear in this rejection of the anatomist's penetration of the human body. As we have seen, Ruskin had become first Slade Professor of Art at Oxford, delivering his first series of lectures in 1870. His appointment was largely due to his old friend Henry Acland, who by this time had risen to become Regius Professor of Medicine and Professor of Clinical Medicine. But Ruskin's behaviour at Oxford – and the truth was that he was heading towards the first of a series of mental breakdowns, in 1878, that were gradually to incapacitate him – became increasingly embarrassing to his supporters at Oxford. In a public lecture he compared the drawings of Michaelangelo, of which the University had a fine collection, unfavourably with those of Tintoretto, and blamed Tintoretto's downfall on the influence of Michaelangelo's study of anatomy. He followed this with a series of lectures titled 'The Relation of Natural Science to Art', summarizing their argument as being that 'the study of anatomy is destructive to art' (22.121). Ruskin showered the University with gifts of paintings, prints and drawings and in 1875 formally endowed his own school of drawing, which continues to teach fine art at the University to this day. But the purpose of the school was, he wrote, to demonstrate 'my new elements of drawing, of which the first vital principle is that man is intended to *observe* with his eyes, and mind; not with microscope and knife' (25.xxx).

As it happens, Acland was one of the first to introduce the use of microscopes in teaching at Oxford. Ruskin delivered several of his courses in a lecture room at the Oxford Museum, for it was more convenient for showing drawings and diagrams. It must have been particularly galling for Acland to have Ruskin describe the Museum as 'a very shabby bit of work of mine' (22.523), or complain that the Museum had been 'filled with dead men's bones, and not only with the bones of men dead, but the bones of men dead by disease for chief subjects of this modern theoretic faculty' (22.513).

Those last two complaints come from the last series of lectures that Ruskin was able to give before his first mental breakdown in 1878 caused him to resign his Professorship. Yet in spite of further attacks, in 1882 he felt well enough to resume his duties. Unfortunately he returned in March 1883 to an Oxford riven by controversy on the issue of vivisection. Acland, ever anxious to enhance the teaching of science, had secured the election of Sir John Burdon-Sanderson as the first Waynflete Professor of Physiology, but he had been battling to persuade the University's Convocation to release the necessary funds to equip a laboratory for him, which would be built at the Museum. The argument was, as usual, about money, but much was made by the opposition of the fact that Professor Sanderson held a licence to practice vivisection. Sanderson declared he had no intention of using it in his teaching, but he would not guarantee that he would not use vivisection in private research. As Acland's biographer J. B. Atlay put it – punning unintentionally – 'it was now war to the knife'.[17]

Ruskin was among those who put their names to a petition to prevent the equipping and maintenance of the new laboratories. In December 1884 his last two lectures of the term were advertised as 'The Pleasures of Sense (Science)' and the 'Pleasures of Nonsense (Atheism)', and it became known that he intended to use them to attack vivisection. He was dissuaded by Acland and his friends, but he could not resist – according to a report of the lectures that he gave instead – telling his audience assembled in the lecture theatre of the Ox-

---

17 J. B. Atlay, *Sir Henry Wentworth Acland, A Memoir* (London: Smith, Elder, 1903), p. 423.

ford Museum that 'these lectures had so far "fluttered the dovecots of the vivi-sectionists" that there had been threats of the intervention of a Board of Stud-ies, and of the incarceration of their single-handed antagonist' (33.523). He wrote in December 1884: 'The scientists slink out of my way now, as if I were a mad dog, for I let them have it hot and heavy whenever I've a chance at them' (37.501). But the anti-vivisectionists were defeated, and Ruskin, already at odds with the University over other matters, felt he had no option but to resign. He told his cousin: 'I cannot lecture in the next room to a shrieking cat – nor address myself to the men who have been – there's no word for it.'[18]

Ruskin's resignation from Oxford in March 1885 marks the beginning of his gradual withdrawal from public life, as his mental attacks became more frequent and more debilitating. What was left of his strength he put into composing his autobiography, *Præterita*, which he began to issue in parts from 1885 onwards. The autobiography was never finished, but he was able to write enough to regain, imaginatively at least, the childhood paradise he describes in the early chapters, with its evocations of tours in Britain and abroad, – 'those first joyful excursions among the Cumberland lakes, which formed my love of landscape and of painting' (26.243) – of the joys of drawing and mineral collecting, and all the magnificence of a world that had not yet been invaded by the knife or microscope.

The story of Ruskin and science is not, then, a happy one, and though one may well sympathize with his moral stance on vivisection, we have to ask ourselves whether there is anything that can be saved, now that what we have learnt from Darwin's tree of scientific knowledge means that we are all banished from Ruskin's garden of natural theology.

First of all, it is good to be reminded by Ruskin's 'science of the aspects of things' of the mental – and moral – discipline imposed by the emphasis on accurate observation as the foundation of all knowledge. That may be a truism for the observational sciences, but it is just as much a requirement in the arts, where not only are we in danger of forgetting how to look, but accuracy of reporting may sometimes be the victim of the desire to impose an idea. Sec-ondly, and in that spirit, we have to recognize that Ruskin's science was not science as it is now formally recognized and defined. Nonetheless, he was try-ing to supply that imaginative, emotional – if you like, spiritual – dimension that he believed neutral observation on its own could not supply. As he said in

---

18 Letter to Joan Severn, quoted in *The Ruskin Art Collection at Oxford: The Rudimentary Series*, ed. Robert Hewison (London: Lion and Unicorn, 1984), p. 33.

one of his last lectures at Oxford: 'I shall not tell you how long a bird's larynx is, for I don't know and I don't care, but I can tell you something about its singing' (33.523–24).

Finally, as is so often the case with Ruskin, there is a sense in which his arguments are a means by which science and the arts reach a synthesis on a higher plane, in terms of man's moral relationship with nature. As Frederick Kirchhoff has written: 'The end of Ruskin's science is neither man's intellectual dominance over the natural world nor his own submission to the dominance of natural law. It is, in Carlyle's terms, "love" – a "virtuous relation" between equals.'[19] As Ruskin has said: 'Nor is it even just to speak of the love of beauty as in all respects unscientific' (5.387).

Both Ruskin and the scientists were trying to communicate a 'truth to Nature': in Ruskin's century it was hoped that the recovery of this truth would be the answer to the consequences of industrialization and all its attendant evils. As our own century draws to a close, how even more pressing it is to rediscover a 'virtuous relation' with the natural world on which we still depend.

As Ruskin told a friend in 1884: 'The *real* scientific man is one who can embrace not only the laws that be, but who can feel to the full the beauty and truth of all that nature has to show, as the Creator made them' (26.xxxix*n*).

19   Frederick Kirchhoff, 'A Science against Sciences: Ruskin's Floral Mythology', in *Nature and the Victorian Imagination*, ed. V. C. Knoeplmacher and G. B. Tennyson (Berkeley: University of California Press, 1977), p. 247.

3

'The Eagle and the Whale?'

John Ruskin's argument with John Tyndall

FRANCIS O'GORMAN

REDERIC HARRISON[1] wrote in 1902 that Ruskin's protracted, public and one-sided argument with John Tyndall (1820–93), the Royal Institution's Professor of Natural Philosophy from 1853–87, was 'like the fabled combat between the eagle and the whale':[2] both men, in other words, inhabited irreconcilably different territory. Ashmore Wingate, eight years afterwards, observed that the on-going dispute, found principally in the pages of *Fors Clavigera* (1871–84) and *Deucalion* (1875–83), was a 'controversy ... just about as unsatisfactory as the affair with Whistler, and nobody got much benefit from it, but only harm: a large section of the public becoming more confirmed than ever in the idea that Ruskin was a dangerous firebrand.'[3] Ruskin's attacks on a leading figure of science (of whom he knew something at first hand through the Metaphysical Society[4]) did not impress his early biographers and they caused some embarrassment to his editors (25.xliv); indeed, his particularly vigorous assault upon Tyndall's views on glaciation in the *Fors Clavigera* letter of October 1873 had even prompted harsh words from his friend Carlyle.[5] But the significance

1   This paper is a version of one delivered to the Ruskin Programme at Lancaster University on 4 February 1995; I am grateful to Professor Michael Wheeler for the initial invitation and to all members of the programme who joined in the discussion which followed. I record my thanks in addition to Dr Dinah Birch, Dr Tess Cosslett, Mr James S. Dearden, Dr Kate Flint, Professor Mark Francis, Mrs Irena McCabe and Dr Bernard Richards. The errors that remain are, of course, my own.

2   Frederic Harrison, *John Ruskin* (London: Macmillan, 1902), p. 158.

3   Ashmore Wingate, *Life of John Ruskin* (London: Scott, 1910), p. 165.

4   See Alan Willard Brown, *The Metaphysical Society: Victorian Minds in Crisis, 1869–1880* (New York: Columbia University Press, 1947).

of Ruskin's argument against Tyndall has been looked at afresh in recent years and it has been found to yield more rewarding matter than those early assessments had allowed. The most extensive recent publication on the topic is Paul Sawyer's revisionary essay 'Ruskin and Tyndall: The Poetry of Matter and the Poetry of Spirit' (1981) in which Sawyer claims, entirely against the grain of conventional views, that 'few incidents in Victorian literature are so rich in implication'.[6] By drawing attention to the closeness of some of Tyndall's thought to Ruskin's, Sawyer adeptly shows the dispute as illuminating 'a crucial intersection in Victorian culture: the intersection of Romantic tradition with the triumph of scientific naturalism'.[7] The aim of the present essay is to continue the revisionary readings of the Ruskin-Tyndall debate and to show in detail that its implications, both for an understanding of Ruskin himself and in terms of wider cultural issues, are in fact even richer than Sawyer acknowledged.

This essay begins with an introductory discussion of what is revealed about Ruskin's argumentative method in the dispute with Tyndall; I then move on to analyse in detail Ruskin's need for certainty and dependability of knowledge in the late science text books, *Love's Meinie* (1873–81), *Deucalion* and *Proserpina* (1875–86), a need closely linked to his desire for abiding moral truths.[8] I argue that, in a variety of different ways, Tyndall's work, like Darwin's, suggested problematic notions of flux, uncertainty and ceaseless change to Ruskin and that this is a major issue in Ruskin's argument with him. The dispute with Tyndall, therefore, involved Ruskin's protest against what he perceived to be a changing intellectual climate which threatened certainty itself and the existence of enduring values. I conclude by observing, however, that some notions of flux and process, though repudiated in one way via the spurning of Tyndall, are in other ways strongly relevant to Ruskin's own writing in the late science books.

5   See Francis O'Gorman, 'Ruskin's *Fors Clavigera* of October 1873: An Unpublished Letter from Carlyle to Tyndall', forthcoming in *Notes and Queries*. For a reassessment of the conventional view of the Carlyle–Ruskin friendship see E. K. Goreau, 'Carlyle and Ruskin: The Private Side of the Public Coin', *Victorian Newsletter*, 46 (1974), 15–19. There is a detailed account of Tyndall and the glacial controversy in J. S. Rowlinson, 'The Theory of Glaciers', *Notes and Records of the Royal Society of London*, 26 (1971), 189–204.

6   Paul L. Sawyer, 'Ruskin and Tyndall: The Poetry of Matter and the Poetry of Spirit', in *Victorian Science and Victorian Values: Literary Perspectives*, ed. James Paradis and Thomas Postlewait (New Brunswick: Rutgers University Press, 1981), pp. 217–46 (p. 217). Other recent work which discusses the Ruskin-Tyndall controversy includes Greg Myers, 'Nineteenth-Century Popularizations of Thermodynamics and the Rhetoric of Social Prophecy', *Victorian Studies*, 29 (1985), 35–66 and Francis O'Gorman, 'Ruskin's Late Science', unpublished doctoral thesis, University of Oxford, 1994, pp. 222–29, 281–316.

7   Sawyer, p. 217.

8   John Unrau discusses Ruskin's use of the word 'moral' and its various connotations in 'Ruskin's Use of the Adjective "Moral"', *English Studies*, 52 (1981), 339–47.

Firstly, then, I wish to argue that the Ruskin-Tyndall dispute reveals a feature of Ruskin's argumentative method, his need for sharp definitions and for the clarity of unblurred oppositions. His treatment of Tyndall is marked in places by a desire to construct in extreme terms, to chisel more sharply the contours of difference. Tyndall in some of Ruskin's presentations is the man whose work threatens the basis of an understanding of the world in divine terms. In *The Eagle's Nest* (1872), for instance, Ruskin had referred critically to Tyndall's belief that the sun was the source of life and that solar heat was ultimately the real power of creation (22.196). In *Deucalion* he further observes that the discovery 'that all mortal strength is from the sun' has 'thrown irrational persons into stupid atheism, as if there were no God but the sun' (26.183). The scientific work upon the sun's generative power, linked so strongly in *The Eagle's Nest* with Tyndall, is associated here with an arid, godless materialism (it was also to be associated with another source of anxiety in the Victorian period as I note later). The charge of Tyndall's godlessness was made in the 1870s by readers much more frankly and much more frequently than by Ruskin: the anonymous author of the uncompromising pamphlet *Materialistic Views of Professor Tyndall and Miss Harriet Martineau Criticized* (1879), for example, thought both Tyndall and Martineau the fruit of the same withering tree, '"The boundless Upas, the all-blasting tree," the tree of Atheism',[9] whilst the atheistic Professor who bluntly declares 'God does not exist' in W.H.Mallock's satirical *The New Paul and Virginia* (1878) significantly allies himself with the 'sublime Tyndall' at the beginning of the novel.[10] Henry Larkin, in his anonymous *Extra Physics* (1878), provided a detailed interrogation of Tyndall's statement that all life came from the sun and found it ultimately lacking in clear meaning.[11] However, the specific label of atheist (not always a precise term in the nineteenth century), which is sometimes still applied at Tyndall,[12] oversimplifies the thinking and beliefs of a much more complex man.

---

9 Anon., *Materialistic Views of Professor Tyndall and Miss Harriet Martineau Criticized* (London: Bickers, 1879), p. v.

10 W. H. Mallock, *The New Paul and Virginia; or, Positivism on an Island,* 2nd edn (London: Chatto, Windus, 1878), pp. 16–17, 18.

11 [Henry Larkin], *Extra Physics and the Mystery of Creation: Including a Brief Examination of Professor Tyndall's Admissions Concerning the Human Soul* (London: Hodder, Stoughton, 1878), pp. 18–25. Dinah Birch examines the significance of Ruskin's ideas about the sun in '"The Sun is God": Ruskin's Solar Mythology', in *The Sun is God: Painting, Literature and Mythology in the Nineteenth Century*, ed. J. B. Bullen (Oxford: Clarendon, 1989), pp. 109–23.

12 See, for instance, Gillian Beer, 'Wave Theory and the Rise of Literary Modernism', in *Realism and Representation: Essays on the Problem of Realism in Relation to Science, Literature and Culture*, ed. George Levine (Madison: University of Wisconsin Press, 1993), p. 207.

Throughout some of his public and private writing at least, Tyndall was neither confident that materialism did explain the existence of life on earth nor scornful of what he carefully called religious feeling. I shall show in a forthcoming study how one of Tyndall's poems of 1892[13] – for Tyndall, like Huxley, was a poet as well as a man of science – clarified an essential agnosticism in his late years and his acceptance of a desire to worship. Here I want to underline more generally the point that uncertainty with regard to the ultimate questions of creation was a recognizable Tyndallian posture despite his bold denunciations of the church and his polemical descriptions of what he saw to be religion's oppressive grip upon the mind of man. He declared in the famous 'Scientific Use of the Imagination' lecture (1870), for example, that the true scientist has 'as little fellowship with the atheist who says there is no God, as with the theist who professes to know the mind of God.'[14] Indeed, such was Tyndall's reluctance to make absolute materialist statements that he was even prepared to contribute in 1876 a short prefatory Note to A. D. White's *The Warfare of Science*, a book which ultimately argued for a future in which science and religion would work together 'ministering through earth God's richest blessings'.[15] Tyndall's theological position was never as assured or clearly definable as Sawyer's claim that he was a 'muscular Christian',[16] but the implication in Ruskin's comments that Tyndall's work simply compelled atheism is an oversimplification, a mis-statement of Tyndall's more complex position.[17]

What is seen in Ruskin's argument, then, is a characteristic procedure and one found elsewhere in *Love's Meinie, Deucalion* and *Proserpina*, in which Ruskin facilitates the clarity of his own position by sharpening and re-focusing the position of the person he desires to make his opponent. Ruskin, in those texts, seeks to present himself as the interpreter of a divinely fashioned nature in which moral truths are persistently articulated to those who have eyes to see them. To underline the plainness of this position he therefore refashions Tyndall as a clearer opponent, as one of the whole benighted collective of modern materialistic scientists whose 'vile industries and vicious curiosities' (25.56) are,

13 See Francis O'Gorman, 'John Tyndall as Poet: Agnosticism and "A Morning on Alp Lusgen"', forthcoming in *Review of English Studies*.

14 John Tyndall, *Fragments of Science: A Series of Detached Essays, Addresses, and Reviews*, 7th edn, 2 vols (London: Longmans, Green, 1889), II, 134.

15 A. D. White, *The Warfare of Science* (London: King, 1876), p. 151.

16 Sawyer, p. 243.

17 For further analysis of Tyndall's religious position see Mark Francis, 'Herbert Spencer and the Mid-Victorian Scientists', *Metascience: Annual Review of the Australasian Association for the History, Philosophy and Social Studies of Science*, 4 (1986), 2–21 (pp. 9–14).

according to Ruskin, blasting the world with fearful chemistries and threatening the spiritual life of human beings. Authority thrives upon opposition and Ruskin must heighten the latter to strengthen the former. Something of the same can be seen again in the late science books in Ruskin's complex negotiations with Darwin and Darwinism. In the 1870s and 1880s Ruskin rejected the materialist implications of evolution repeatedly – 'God makes gentians gay and lichens grave as it pleases Him, and by no other law, no other reason' (37.140) he told Dawtrey Drewitt crossly in 1874 – but he *also* rejects or at the very least passes silently over Darwinian ideas, emphasized by other contemporary readers, which one would have thought he might have found at least a little more sympathetic. Ruskin does not, for instance, pick up upon Darwin's ideas about the presence within nature of absolutely inflexible laws which proved so attractive to many theistic readers, and neither does he have anything to say about Darwin's underlying conception of the unity and organic wholeness of the living world.[18] Ruskin's fundamental acceptance of unity and oneness was certainly different from Darwin's[19], but one might have expected *some* notice of this broadly shared idea of interconnectedness in Ruskin's comments.[20] Yet it is clear that the need for decisive distinctions and for the uncompromised and unqualified maintenance of Ruskin's own oppositional authority impinges upon his response to Darwin as it did markedly in his reaction to Tyndall.

Ruskin's dispute with Tyndall reveals an aspect of his construction of authority in the science books. But the argument is also a major campaign ground in Ruskin's complex and contradictory battle against, but also fascination with, slippage, instability and impermanence. If the three science text books of the 1870s and '80s have a prevalent concern which runs like a backbone throughout them, it is with the teaching of certainty and, ultimately, with the maintenance of durable values and permanent truths against anything, scientific or otherwise, which threatens them. Ruskin's desire (a complex and inconsistent one, as I shall show) to insist upon a world of stable and dependable truths in which, essentially, moral and spiritual verities are enduring, burns brightly

---

18 For discussion of scientific ideas of law and the organic see Tess Cosslett, *The 'Scientific Movement' and Victorian Literature* (Brighton: Harvester, 1982), especially pp. 15–17 and pp. 21–25 respectively.

19 There is extended discussion of Ruskin's distinctive conception of the organic in James Clerk Sherburne, *John Ruskin; or, the Ambiguities of Abundance: A Study in Social and Economic Criticism* (Cambridge, MA: Harvard University Press, 1972).

20 Further discussions of Ruskin's disagreement with Darwin can be found in C. S. Finley, 'Ruskin, Darwin, and the Crisis of Natural Form', *Cahiers Victoriens et Edouardiens,* 25 (1987), 7–24 and O'Gorman (1994), pp. 113–192.

throughout *Love's Meinie, Deucalion* and *Proserpina*, and it is a desire which impinges heavily upon his negotiations with Tyndall. It is this issue which I shall discuss in some detail here. Ruskin's suspicion of flux, inconstancy and process is, however, no straightforward one and, as I shall conclude this essay by showing, Ruskin's own scientific work is itself implicated within that very suspicion. I shall indicate, not least, how Ruskin is paradoxically fascinated by and drawn to the language of flux and inconstancy, sometimes exploiting productively and vividly the lexis of a viewpoint apparently very different from his own.

Ruskin's science books are offered as the source of certain knowledge, as 'grammars ... which will contain nothing but indisputable facts' (28.647). This is a particularly prominent claim of *Deucalion* which, Ruskin said, 'is authoritative as far as it reaches, and will stand out like a quartz dyke, as the sandy speculations of modern gossiping geologists get washed away' (25.413). Of its purpose, Ruskin also declared 'I am resolved ... to make the series of *Deucalion* an absolutely trustworthy foundation for the geological teaching in St. George's schools; by sifting what is really known from what is supposed; and then, out of things known, sifting what may be usefully taught to young people, from the perplexed vanity of prematurely systematic science' (26.197). His desire for certainty of knowledge, which is linked to his praise of obedience to dependable and trustworthy authority in the Guild of St George, is also expressed as a suspicion of what he calls scientific theory and a dislike of debate in the science text books. When scientific knowledge becomes uncertain and blurred, in Ruskin's view, it 'fades into theory' (26.233) and he proclaims at the end of the first chapter of *Deucalion,* in words which are intended to inaugurate the task of the remainder of the text, that 'we must begin where all theory ceases' (26.112). Theory and hypothesisation must be replaced by certitude in Ruskin's conception and thus he boldly declares: 'I never theorize, I give you the facts only' (26.109). Ruskin's insistence that he can offer 'facts' strikes us now as a naïve one but his belief that modern science dealt in 'theories' rather than 'facts' relates suggestively to the increasing sense amongst some scientists themselves in the second half of the nineteenth century (though many would have rejected the actual term 'scientist'[21]) that science did indeed advance via useful fictions

21 See Sydney Ross, '*Scientist:* The Story of a Word', *Annals of Science,* 18 (1962), 65–85.

22 See, for instance, Peter Allan Dale, 'George Lewes' Scientific Aesthetic: Restructuring the Ideology of the Symbol', in *One Culture: Essays in Science and Literature,* ed. George Levine (Madison: University of Wisconsin Press, 1987), pp. 92–116 and Alexander Welsh, 'Theories of Science and Romance, 1870–1920', *Victorian Studies,* 17 (1973), 135–54. For discussions of issues relating more generally to realism and fact in science see, for instance, George Levine, 'Looking for the Real: Epistemology in Science and Culture', in Levine (1993), pp. 3–23;

or was in fact centrally preoccupied with them.[22] Of debate and discussion in science Ruskin is similarly dismissive, claiming that disputation is an activity 'idler than the chafed pebbles of the wavering beach' (26.154) and something which should always be rejected in favour of the teaching of certain fact. 'For us', he says at the beginning of *Deucalion*, 'let the facts at least be clear ... but all debate declined' (26.106). Such a repudiation of discussion in science, it should be added, is related to Ruskin's dissatisfaction with and criticism of Liberalism and Millite free-thinking most clearly apparent in *Fors Clavigera* in the 1870s, a topic analysed in detail by Judith Stoddart who has endeavoured to place *Fors* within the context of wider Victorian political debates.[23]

Ruskin's science books aspire to teach certain facts which are dependable, stable and abiding. The requirement for the constant, dependable and permanent in science, however, attains a much wider significance when it plays a part in Ruskin's reception of Darwinism, for here it is eventually augmented into an issue which concerns nothing less than the persistence of absolute values. Even when using Darwin for witty, satirical purposes in *Fors Clavigera*, Ruskin is drawn to the idea of species transformation, to the instability of particular identity. In the *Fors* letter for May 1873, for instance, he uses species relationship and species distinction to critical ends, observing that the new middle classes of London live in houses which resemble brick railway carriages and that they are like 'monkeys that have lost the use of their legs'. Further scientific language follows making an unexpected point: 'The baboons in Regent's Park', Ruskin says, ' – with Mr. Darwin's pardon – *are* of another species; a less passive, and infinitely wittier one' (27.531). This playful comment – though one perhaps darkened, as I have suggested elsewhere, by an allusion to a vision of the underworld in Blake's *The Marriage of Heaven and Hell*[24] – is one of a series of examples in which Ruskin's references to Darwin involve the idea of the mutability of species, species transformation or species relationship.[25] But it is a preoccupation which, beneath the wit, has profoundly serious resonances for him.

Gillian Beer, 'Problems of Description in the Language of Discovery', in Levine (1987), pp. 35–58 and Evelyn Fox Keller, *Secrets of Life, Secrets of Death: Essays on Language, Gender and Science* (New York: Routledge, 1992), especially pp. 1–12.

23 Judith Stoddart, 'The Rhetoric of Reform: John Ruskin's *Fors Clavigera* and the Politics of the 1870s', unpublished doctoral thesis, University of Oxford, 1990; for more on the place of *Fors* in contemporary political debate see Stoddart's essay 'The Formation of the Working Classes: John Ruskin's *Fors Clavigera* as a Manual of Cultural Literacy', *Bucknell Review*, 34 (1990), 43–58.

24 Francis O'Gorman, 'A Blakean Allusion in Ruskin's *Fors Clavigera*', *Notes and Queries*, n.s. 42 (1995), 175–76.

25 Other examples include 27.130–31, 27.657, 28.154, 28.466.

In his comments upon Darwinian species development in *The Queen of the Air* (1869) those weightier issues and their markedly serious implications emerge more clearly. There, Ruskin sets aside ideas of the constant process of evolutionary activity (the very thing which had attracted Walter Pater)[26] in order to focus instead upon what he saw as the necessary distinctness of species and, vitally, of the moral truths they embodied:

> Whatever the origin of species may be, or however those species, once formed, may be influenced by external accident, the groups into which birth or accident reduce them have distinct relation to the spirit of man. It is perfectly possible, and ultimately conceivable, that the crocodile and the lamb may have descended from the same ancestral atom of protoplasm; and that the physical laws of the operation of calcareous slime and of meadow grass, on that protoplasm, may in time have developed the opposite natures and aspects of the living frames; but the practically important fact for us is the existence of a power which creates that calcareous earth itself; – which creates that, separately, and quartz, separately, and gold, separately, and charcoal, separately; and then so directs the relations of these elements that the gold may destroy the souls of men by being yellow; and the charcoal destroy their souls by being hard and bright; and the quartz represent to them an ideal purity; and the calcareous earth, soft, may beget crocodiles, and dry and hard, sheep; and the aspects and qualities of these two products, crocodiles and lambs, may be, the one repellent to the spirit of man, the other attractive to it, in a quite inevitable way, representing to him states of moral evil and good, and becoming myths to him of destruction or redemption, and, in the most literal sense, 'Words' of God. (19.358–59)

For Ruskin here, arguing with Darwinism or at least side-stepping his science is a protest against nothing less than a changing intellectual climate in which flux, change itself and, in the wings perhaps, the fearsome spectre of relativity, threaten the permanence of enduring values and permanent moral truths. The living '"Words" of God' must be preserved in their integrity, separate and distinct; independent from the properly irrelevant issues of development, change and ancestral relationship.

The requirement for certainty, the rejection of flux and the need for a science 'founded on eternal facts'[27] impinges, I suggest, heavily upon Ruskin's reception of Tyndall. Tyndall is a presence who must be jousted with, challenged

---

26 See, for instance, Walter Pater, *Plato and Platonism: A Series of Lectures*, Library Edition (London: Macmillan, 1910), p. 19.

27 Letter to Daniel Oliver about botany, 19 January 1875, quoted in Dinah Birch, 'Ruskin and the Science of *Proserpina*', in *New Approaches to Ruskin: Thirteen Essays*, ed. Robert Hewison (London: Routledge, Paul, 1981), 142–56 (p. 152).

and subdued in the pages of *Deucalion* because in a variety of different ways his thought and his very prose could be linked, as perceived from Ruskin's distinctive point of view, to unwanted ideas of process, impermanence and transitoriness.

This whole polygonal issue may be seen first in what Tyndall has to say about the culturally routine idea in Victorian England of the progress of science. In general terms Tyndall accepts the scientific, Comtean commonplace that humanity has progressed from a reading of the natural phenomena in a supernatural or mythical mode towards an understanding of the world in empirical terms. The progress of empirical science itself is frequently presented in his writing as a pattern of accretion in which the data and theories of one group of scientists prepare the way for the bolder generalizations of others who are nonetheless indebted to the earlier work. In the notorious 'Belfast Address' of August 1874, for instance, Tyndall observes how the work of Galileo and Kepler provided the preparation for Newton's theory of gravity later on.[28] At other times, however, Tyndall more strikingly presents the progress of science (and it is certainly progressive in his conception) as a narrative which periodically involves dramatic changes in scientific understanding which of necessity require the modification or overthrowing of prior beliefs. Tyndall at times agrees that new scientific explanations require radical reassessment of former convictions and, indeed, he goes some of the way towards anticipating Kuhn's argument that the movement of scientific understanding is 'an intrinsically revolutionary process' in which new hypotheses require 'the reconstruction of prior theory and the re-evaluation of prior fact'.[29] Such a position, which differed markedly, for instance, from Ray Lankester's conviction argued before the British Association in 1871 that, in terms of the development of scientific ideas, 'the new is built on and incorporates the old',[30] problematizes implicitly the nature of scientific certainty, for it raises the possibility that what is constitutive of accepted orthodoxy today may become itself vulnerable to subsequent comprehensive revision in a potentially continuous pattern of reappraisal.

The history of science in Tyndall's narrations turns periodically on significant moments of considerable change and his clearest example is in fact one also offered by Kuhn.[31] Tyndall dwells in *Six Lectures on Light* (1873) at some length

---

28 *Fragments,* II, p. 155.

29 Thomas Kuhn, *The Structure of Scientific Revolutions,* 2nd edn (Chicago: Chicago University Press, 1970), p. 7.

30 E. Ray Lankester, *The Advancement of Science: Occasional Essays and Addresses* (London: Macmillan, 1890), p. 108.

31 Kuhn, pp. 11–12.

upon Olav Roemer's discovery in 1676 that light moved at a measurable speed; by this realization, Tyndall notes, 'the notion entertained by Descartes, and espoused by Hooke, that light is propagated instantly through space, was overthrown'.[32] Roemer's new conception of optical physics – his measurement of the speed of light, Tyndall notes, had to be amended subsequently – changes prior belief dramatically in a way which Tyndall finds elsewhere in the history of science. In *The Forms of Water* (1872), he likewise observes that even Newton cherished a view – that light consisted of 'elastic particles of inconceivable minuteness shot out with inconceivable rapidity by luminous bodies'[33] – which Tyndall believed to be erroneous and to have been subsequently overthrown by the wave theory.[34] (As for other scientists at the same time,[35] one should note, the debate about wave theory and particle theory brings to the surface in Tyndall's mind the issue of the presence, essentially, of the fictive within empirical science for he observes that the wave theory cannot, in the present state of knowledge, be demonstrably proved and that he is talking of 'suppositions and assumptions merely',[36] however compelling they may be.) In the 'Belfast Address', finally, Tyndall is drawn to another telling moment when new scientific understanding radically revises the past: Copernicus's 'epoch-making work … on the paths of heavenly bodies' in 1543, which, he notes, brought about the 'total crash of Aristotle's closed universe, with the earth at its centre'.[37] Reading from Ruskin's distinctive standpoint with his requirement for science to teach certainty and truths which are confidently and authoritatively known, Tyndall's mode of narration periodically presents scientific knowledge as implicitly problematic, for the story of the progress of empirical science involves, it seems, occasional dramatic changes of accepted and apparently durable beliefs.

Tyndall's narrations of the history of science sometimes dwell upon change in a pattern which is at once progressive and also which involves moments of sharp re-orientation. But the broader, more generalized idea of motion, of change, of transformation, impinges upon Tyndall's science in a more sustained

32 John Tyndall, *Six Lectures on Light Delivered in America in 1872–1873* (London: Longmans, Green, 1873), p. 23.

33 Ibid., p. 45.

34 John Tyndall, *The Forms of Water in Clouds and Rivers, Ice and Glaciers* (London: King, 1872), p. 9. For a discussion of Newtonian ideas and their partial revival in the twentieth century see Norwood Russell Hanson, 'Waves, Particles, and Newton's "Fits"', *Journal of the History of Ideas*, 21 (1960), 370–91.

35 See Welsh, p. 139.

36 *The Forms of Water*, p. 10.

37 *Fragments*, II, 153.

and thorough way elsewhere, for his whole conception of the universe itself is a Helmholtzian one: the idea of ceaseless flux is central to it. Greg Myers has observed how closely the principle of the conservation of energy was associated 'in the popular mind with the name of John Tyndall'[38] and Tyndall lectured extensively expounding its significance. It was a doctrine which, as others have shown, Tyndall found anticipated in the writings of Thomas Carlyle,[39] the man whom he called elsewhere 'one of the glories of the world'.[40] Tyndall's analyses of the implications of the conservation of energy doctrine, the theory which Frank Turner has described as 'probably more destructive to a supernatural interpretation of nature than was evolution by natural selection',[41] emphasize the constant change and unremitting restlessness of the universe amidst the quantitative constancy of its energy. The amount of energy circulating through the world is fixed but its movement is ceaseless. Thus Tyndall noted in 'Science and Man' (1877): 'This doctrine [of the conservation of energy] recognizes in the material universe a constant sum of power made up of items among which the most Protean fluctuations are incessantly going on. It is as if the body of Nature were alive, the thrill and interchange of its energies resembling those of an organism. The parts of the "stupendous whole" shift and change, augment and diminish, appear and disappear … '.[42] The seemingly organic whole of the world thrills endlessly with constant movement.

In 1865, in 'The Constitution of Nature', Tyndall similarly stressed the never-ending process of the world: 'We on the earth's surface', he noted, 'live night and day in the midst of ethereal commotion. The medium is never still'.[43] Tyndall's belief in the persistent 'flux of power',[44] the buzzing interchange of the world's energies, even has some place in the opening lines of his 1892 poem 'A Morning on Alp Lusgen':

---

38 Myers, p. 42.

39 See Frank M. Turner, 'John Tyndall and Victorian Scientific Naturalism' and Anna Therese Cosslett, 'Science and Value: The Writings of John Tyndall', in *John Tyndall: Essays on a Natural Philosopher*, ed. W. H. Brock, N. D. McMillan and R. C. Mollan (Dublin: Royal Dublin Society, 1981), pp. 169–180 and 181–91 respectively.

40 John Tyndall, *New Fragments* (London: Longmans, Green, 1892), p. 391.

41 Frank M. Turner, *Between Science and Religion: The Reaction to Scientific Naturalism in Late Victorian England* (New Haven: Yale University Press, 1974), p. 27. There is a straightforward introduction to energy theories in the Victorian period in J. A. V. Chapple, *Science and Literature in the Nineteenth Century* (London: Macmillan, 1986), pp. 43–49.

42 *Fragments*, II, 340.

43 *Fragments*, I, 8.

44 John Tyndall, *Heat: A Mode of Motion*, 7th edn (London: Longmans, Green, 1887), p. 536.

The sun has cleared the peaks and quenched the flush
Of orient crimson with excess of light.
The tall grass quivers in the rhythmic air
Without a sound; yet each particular blade
Trembles in song, had we but ears to hear.[45]

– where a portion of the natural description (the 'rhythmic air' and the trembling grass) betrays a Helmholtzian dimension.[46] Tyndall's emphasis upon the flux of the world, moreover, is co-ordinated occasionally with the more extreme idea of dissolution, with the notion of the illusoriness of material solidity and the impermanence of actuality. Part of the prefatory quotation from Emerson at the beginning of the published version of the 'Scientific Use of the Imagination' lecture suggests as much:

The rushing metamorphosis
Dissolving all that fixture is,
Melts things that be to things that seem,
And solid nature to a dream.[47]

This Emersonian dissolution is the extreme point of the world's changefulness where the tangible and actual are seen as chimerical and things in themselves cease to be anything but illusory.

Tyndall's conception of the universe and his expositions of the theory of the conservation of energy speak persistently of that which is in motion and of ceaseless transformation. From the point of view of the main trajectory and the dominant imperatives and ambitions of Ruskin's own scientific books, such a world of change and alteration – even within the midst of the quantitative consistency of energy – is ill-favoured and unwanted and thus must form one of the compelling factors in Ruskin's rejection of Tyndall.

At the very end of Ruskin's creative life, it should be added, something of what I am suggesting he sensed intuitively in Tyndall's writing came to face Ruskin in a rather more explicit way, and it was, unsurprisingly, to be spurned. At the beginning of 1885 Ruskin entered a correspondence with Professor (later Sir) Oliver Lodge[48] broadly about the nature of clouds and vapour; Lodge's reply to Ruskin's second letter, of 9 February 1885, referred to the 'chief feature of the kinetic theory of gases – the rapid movements of the individual

---

45 *New Fragments*, p. 498.

46 I am indebted to Dr Kate Flint for this observation on Tyndall's verse.

47 *Fragments*, II, 120.

48 In 1881, Oliver Lodge (1851–1940) became Professor of Physics at University College, Liverpool; in 1900 he was appointed Principal of the newly founded Birmingham University.

molecules even in stationary air'[49] and it was, suggestively, to this idea of continual molecular motion that Ruskin's eye was drawn. He was, he told Lodge,
'entirely staggered and appalled' by the 'idea of atoms "jumping out by their
own proper motion – or by blows from below – etc"'[50] and two days later
announced to him firmly: 'Of the molecular motion I thought yesterday till I
was sick and giddy and could eat no dinner. I can't read any books upon it, nor
do I ever concern myself about anything that I cannot see, touch, or feel with
my heart. I come to *you* to give me the *facts* of what I COULD *see* if I chose.'[51]
Scientific ideas involving ceaseless movement and continuous change, whether
instinctively sensed in Tyndall's writings or bluntly faced in Lodge's letters,
generate sustained disapproval and Ruskin's re-assertion of the necessity of
clear, durable and unequivocal fact.

Process and the motionary are resisted in part by the insistence in *Love's
Meinie, Deucalion* and *Proserpina* upon the certainty of particulars and the permanence of the general truths they habitually emblematize; thus the flower, for
example, is pictured in *Proserpina* in strongly moralized and definitive language
as 'the utmost purification of the plant, and the utmost discipline. Where its
tissue is blanched fairest, dyed purest, set in strictest rank, appointed to most
chosen office, there – and created by the fact of this purity and function – is the
flower' (25.249). The resistance to process (though not a straightforward one as
I shall show) and the preference for the emphatic and dependable can even be
sensed behind Ruskin's apparently paradoxical rejection of the very nature of
Tyndall's prose. In the 'Labitur, et Labetur' (1875) chapter of *Deucalion* Ruskin
criticizes the 'general literary structure' (26.143) of Tyndall's *The Glaciers of the
Alps* (1860), complaining of its author's vanity and of the fact that there is too
much of the writer himself in the text. Ruskin's grievance that Tyndall has
failed to discriminate between 'scientific writing' and 'pleasant autobiography'
(26.144) is an unexpected one, however, given the extended presence of autobiography within Ruskin's own science books and there is, I suggest, something
important but quite disguised at stake in this disapproval.

Tyndall's own prose manner in *Glaciers,* his own characteristic mode of narration, habitually foregrounds the *processes* of empirical science, the collection
of facts, the thinking through of consequences and possibilities; it is essentially
an exploratory mode of writing which records a pattern of accretion,

49 J. H. Whitehouse, ed., *Saint George*, 8 (1905), 285.

50 *Saint George*, p. 286.

51 *Saint George*, pp. 286–87.

conjecturalization and anticipation. The following passage, which is characteristic of the first part of Tyndall's text altogether, demonstrates notably the features which lurch so strikingly away from Ruskin's formulation that science books must teach certain knowledge and known fact:

> The points of the glacier beyond my reach I examined through a telescope; along the faces of the sections the lines of stratification were clearly shown; and in many places where the mass showed manifest signs of lateral pressure, I thought I could observe the cleavage passing through the strata. The point, however, was too important to rest upon an observation made from such a distance, and I therefore abstained from mentioning it subsequently. I examined the fissures and the veining, and noticed how the latter became most perfect in places where the pressure was greatest. The effect of *oblique* pressure was also finely shown: at one place the thrust of the descending glacier was opposed by the resistance offered by the side of the valley, the direction of the force being oblique to the side; the consequence was a structure parallel to the valley, and consequently oblique to the thrust which I believe to be its cause.[52]

Tyndall here records his suppositions as he made them, his awareness of the inadequacy of his present state of knowledge and the problems of making deductions from the information he has at his disposal in a text which works so often in the fashion of a diary presenting records of immediate experience. Tyndall summarizes his thoughts as they were at a particular moment within a process, within a narrative of accretion, accounting for each stage of his progression towards what he believes to be reliable facts, competent interpretation and acceptable hypotheses. Tyndall's very prose manner, his 'general literary structure' and its reflection of process, hypothesisation and conjecture is, I propose, decidedly unattractive to Ruskin with his expressed intentions for didactic scientific texts and his ambitions for a reformed, reorientated science which communicates with surety and authority the dependable facts of certain knowledge.

Moreover, in Ruskin's copy of the first edition of *The Forms of Water*, currently at The Ruskin Galleries, Bembridge School, Ruskin has scored or marked heavily a number of passages in which Tyndall is, as it were, thinking aloud in the manner of *The Glaciers* or recording his (scientific) thoughts as they occur to him: the passages clearly involve the idea of uncertainty or concern hypothesis formulation or even open guessing. Ruskin underlines as indicated, for instance,

---

52 John Tyndall, *The Glaciers of the Alps: Being a Narrative of Excursions and Ascents, an Account of the Origin and Phenomena of Glaciers, and an Exposition of the Physical Principles to Which They are Related* (London: Murray, 1860), p. 26.

Tyndall's sentence on page 73: '<u>This is a thought suggested on the spot</u>; it may or <u>it may not be true</u>'; a little later on the same page he marks 'If <u>our surmise</u> be true …'. More emphatically, he places two exclamation marks and adds strong vertical lines besides Tyndall's words on the following page beginning: 'You will here observe that the "guesses" of science are not the work of chance but of thoughtful pondering over antecedent facts.' These annotations – and there are other comparable ones – perhaps further reveal Ruskin's decided impatience with Tyndall's willingness to record thought-processes, first ideas and unverified suppositions as part of his science writing.[53]

Ruskin finds in Tyndall, then, a series of related and connected ideas centring upon the ideas of process, transformation, uncertainty and movement which in part conflict with his own science books' broad aspirations to deal with the certain and the enduring, and which are sharply at odds with the world of secure truths and permanent values so deeply implicated for Ruskin within that conflict. In his engagement with Tyndall it is partly process itself which is the subject and all that that could mean for Ruskin in terms of the security and permanence of truths. Ruskin's *resistance* to Tyndall is the main feature of his engagement with him. But it is not ultimately the only feature. My argument, therefore, must move on to look at the other, less prominent but no less revealing side of what is at times a two-way transaction, a rejection and a fascination, a repelling and an attracting. Certainly Ruskin sometimes endeavours in the late science text books to exploit and productively manipulate the language of process and flux to his own ends, even finding some place, as I shall show, to re-write movingly the tropes of entropy. But the presence of process and the provisional is more than this in *Love's Meinie, Deucalion* and *Proserpina*, for in relevant ways Ruskin's own writing in those books periodically draws attention to process itself even amidst the more prominent aspirations for clarity and authority in the texts' didactic purposes. The central ambition of the books is a desire to teach the certain knowledge of a world of absolute truths, yet alongside this the writing nonetheless makes us periodically aware of the provisional, the incomplete or the very processes involved in reaching out towards the permanence of certainty. The relationship with Tyndall and all that he stood for, then, is not solely an argument between eagle and whale: both men once in a while inhabit shared territory.

---

53 Publication of material held in the Ruskin Galleries, Bembridge School, Isle of Wight, is by courtesy of the Ruskin Foundation. I am indebted to Mr James S. Dearden for his generous help.

Proserpina in particular draws attention a number of times to the arduous nature of its revisionary task of laying out anew the foundations of botanical science. Ruskin's hesitations, his sense of the overwhelming extent of his new Blakean task – 'to construct a system in order to destroy systems'[54] – daunt him. All *Proserpina* can therefore hope to do, Ruskin indicates, is to start the journey towards proper, durable knowledge which is a knowledge of particulars, general laws and abiding truths: it is a prophetic text, a template for future work which is a stage upon a journey. Thus it is that Ruskin, with extreme and provocative irony with regard to his argument with Tyndall, records at one point in Chapter I that 'this book will be nothing but process' (25.216). Process of one kind may be repudiated in the late science – partly via the very censure of Tyndall – but it is also paradoxically a fitting description of aspects of Ruskin's very way of working, particularly in *Proserpina*, and of the sometimes tentative nature – necessitated, he claims, by the backward state of modern science – of that text's gestures towards dependable and proper knowledge. Process as a textual feature is acceptable but only as a stage towards certainty.

But there are more obvious points to be made about process and order, system and certainty, for the science text books in other ways diverge noticeably and dramatically at times from their own repeated requirements for ordered, systematic and unequivocal teaching, and there is a heavy paradox indeed, for instance, involved in their patchy, digressive and incomplete manner or even, more locally, the occasional explicit admission of the confusing and inconsistent nature of their new taxonomic systems.[55] Ruskin's writing, threaded with social criticism and prophecy, theological and personal themes and explicitly autobiographical references, is familiarly multiple and poly-directional even amidst the science books' bolder claims for certitude, authority and the assured teaching of moral verities. Sheila Emerson has commented upon another dimension of this abiding and characteristically Ruskinian paradox, remarking (with particular pertinence to the late science books) that 'No one has ever loathed chaotic deviation more eloquently than Ruskin, but neither has anyone celebrated more powerfully the variety of Nature'.[56] Order and disorder co-

---

54 Frederick Kirchhoff, 'A Science Against Sciences: Ruskin's Floral Mythology', in *Nature and the Victorian Imagination,* ed. U. C. Knoepflmacher and G. B. Tennyson (Berkeley: University of California Press, 1977), p. 247. For a discussion of a different dimension of *Proserpina*'s rejection of modern botany see Beverly Seaton, 'Considering the Lilies: Ruskin's "Proserpina" and Other Victorian Flower Books', *Victorian Studies,* 28 (1985), 255–82.

55 See, for example, 25.352.

56 Sheila Emerson, 'The Authorization of Form: Ruskin and the Science of Chaos', in *Chaos and Order: Complex Dynamics in Literature and Science,* ed. N. Katherine Hayles (Chicago: University of Chicago Press, 1991), pp. 149–66 (p. 152).

exist in the science books; process and development are there even amidst the determined statements of the orderly and systematic, the structured and dependable.

Other more complex dimensions to the response to process and change in *Love's Meinie, Deucalion* and *Proserpina* can be detected. Periodically in the late science books Ruskin delights in using the language of his apparent opponents to his own ends: through mimicking the vocabulary of the oppositional view he can, to borrow appropriate words from Irigaray, convert it 'into an affirmation, and thus begin to thwart it'.[57] Ruskin's annexations of the lexis of evolution, for instance, involve a total transformation of meaning where he re-orientates the language of his opponents to make it articulate the matter of his own distinctive view. This is most evident in the first chapter of volume II of *Deucalion* entitled 'Living Waves', part of which had begun life as a lecture at the London Institution on 17 March 1880. The lecture series itself had been begun by T. H. Huxley who had delivered a paper upon snakes during which he had announced, Ruskin tells us, that a 'serpent is ... a lizard that has dropped his legs off' (26.306). Ruskin, by citing Huxley, allows into his own text, apparently hospitably, the words of an evolutionist (and thus a person Ruskin is more likely to outlaw) but in replying to him Ruskin startlingly outdoes him, borrowing then transforming Huxley's Darwinian vocabulary and forcing it to serve his own very different purposes:

> In the first quarter, or house, of his nativity, a serpent is, as Professor Huxley showed you, a lizard that has dropped his legs off. But in the second quarter, or house, of his nativity, I shall show that he is also a duck that has dropped her wings off. In the third quarter, I shall show you that he is a fish that has dropped his fins off. And in the fourth quarter of ascent, or descent, whichever you esteem it, that a serpent is a honeysuckle, with a head put on. (26.306)

This bravura performance, neatly picking up the language of species development while fusing it with some unexpected astrological vocabulary and even including an apparently careless glance at the ascent/descent debate, has an element of bizarre comedy about it. But it is also a very serious way for Ruskin to talk about the form and movement of the snake – a creature which both fascinated and repelled him and which he drew repeatedly[58] – through a gen-

---

57 Luce Irigaray, *Ce Sexe qui n'en est pas un*, trans. Catherine Porter with Carolyn Burke (Ithaca: Cornell University Press, 1985), p. 76.

58 Marc A. Simpson provides an account of Ruskin's snakes and their significance in 'The Dream of the Dragon: Ruskin's Serpent Imagery', in *The Ruskin Polygon: Essays on the Imagination of John Ruskin*, ed. John Dixon Hunt and Faith M. Holland (Manchester: Manchester University Press, 1982), pp. 21–43.

der-blurring comparison with the form and movement of other living animals and plants. (For example, he goes on to say, a snake is like a honeysuckle in the link between the action of its twisting tendrils and the snake's 'strangling coils' (26.313).) These are provocative species relationships of a very different and, it goes without saying, completely unDarwinian kind; they are affiliations of form and function which in fact stress the specific and individual identities of species, their movements and characteristic natures. Subversive imitation and parody prove productive modes of articulation for Ruskin who, in the original lecture, was even physically inhabiting, at his lecture desk, the space previously occupied by an acclaimed champion of orthodox evolutionary science.

The beginning of *Deucalion* reveals Ruskin also, I suggest, using another kind of scientific language for his own purposes in a way which links across to an idea associated in the later Victorian period with the concepts of flux and change already discussed. The extreme point of some Victorian anxieties about the world's instability and a point where, Gillian Beer remarks, 'Physics, mythography, and the ordinary fear of death'[59] converged, concerned the belief best articulated by William Thomson (later Lord Kelvin) as early as 1852 that, through irreversible energy dissipation, the earth would be 'within a finite period of time to come … unfit for the habitation of man as at present constituted'.[60] This anxiety of thermodynamics was linked to the notion that the sun, which Tyndall had declared the source of all energy necessary for terrestrial life, was progressively dissipating its own energy and therefore irredeemably cooling down. Tyndall's solar physics thus became entangled with another great concern in the second half of the nineteenth century, a concern not only about materialism but also about the veritable extinction of earthly life itself. Literary reactions and responses to this apocalyptic anxiety were manifold,[61] not least because the scientific language of entropy and of the winding down of the earth's energies paradoxically renewed and invigorated familiar, ancient tropes of death. This was true for T. H. Huxley's largely forgotten (and rather awkward) poem 'Westminster Abbey, October 12, 1892' on the death of Tennyson which concludes:

---

59 Gillian Beer, '"The Death of the Sun": Victorian Solar Physics and Solar Myth', in Bullen, 109–23 (p. 159).

60 William Thomson, 'On a Universal Tendency in Nature to the Dissipation of Mechanical Energy', *Philosophical Magazine and Journal of Science*, 4th series, 4 (1852), 304–6 (p. 306).

61 Some are discussed in Beer's '"The Death of the Sun"'; *see also* her 'Origins and Oblivion in Victorian Narrative', in *Sex, Politics, and Science in the Nineteenth Century Novel*, ed. Ruth Bernard Yeazell (Baltimore: Johns Hopkins University Press, 1986), pp. 63–87.

And oh! sad wedded mourner, seeking still
For vanished hand-clasp; drinking in thy fill
Of holy grief: forgive, that pious theft
Robs thee of all, save memories, left:
Not thine to kneel beside the grassy mound
While dies the western glow; and all around
Is silence; and the shadows closer creep
And whisper softly: All must fall asleep.[62]

Huxley's conventional trope of the dying sun and the commonplace 'All must fall asleep' gain freshness from the scientific realization – of which Huxley was vividly aware – that the two, via the discoveries of modern physics, were perhaps profoundly and inevitably connected.

Now *Deucalion* opens with Ruskin's own response to the language and concepts of energy loss in what is perhaps a shadowy gesture towards those culturally familiar anxieties arising from contemporary thermodynamics and solar physics. And, as with the language of evolution, he annexes the terms of energy decay for his own distinctive purposes, turning them here into a reflection upon himself and his own failing state:

I have been glancing lately at many biographies, and have been much struck by the number of deaths which occur between the ages of fifty and sixty (and, for the most part, in the earlier half of the decade), in cases where the brain has been much used emotionally: or perhaps it would be more accurate to say, where the heart, and the faculties of perception connected with it, have stimulated the brain action. Supposing such excitement to be temperate, equable, and joyful, I have no doubt the tendency of it would be to prolong, rather than depress, the vital energies. But the emotions of indignation, grief, controversial anxiety and vanity, or hopeless, and therefore uncontending, scorn, are all of them as deadly to the body as poisonous air or polluted water; and when I reflect how much of the active part of my past life has been spent in these states, – and that what may remain to me of life can never more be in any other, – I begin to ask myself, with somewhat pressing arithmetic, how much time is likely to be left me, at the age of fifty-six, to complete the various designs for which, until past fifty, I was merely collecting materials. (26.95–96)

This introductory passage is not without some passing wit, but its anxiety is nonetheless authentic. Ruskin's concerns about his own age and his own longevity and his sense of potentially failing 'vital energies' in the face of a great burden of uncompleted work constitute, perhaps, his own emotive reworking and melancholy personalization of the idea of entropy in a book which bears

---

62 *Poems of Henrietta Huxley with Three of Thomas Henry Huxley* (n.p.: p.p., 1899), p. 4.

the very word 'lapse' in its subtitle.[63] The closing down of energies thus becomes a painfully personal issue. Two days after dating this introduction from Brantwood, one might add, Ruskin recorded in his diary: 'I utterly depressed and good for nothing' (D, 853).

Ruskin's argument with Tyndall is in part about a resistance to notions of flux, process and transformation, and it is a dispute which therefore takes one into central currents of Ruskin's intellectual condemnation of and hostility towards what he perceived to be dominant issues of modernity. But it is a dispute without clear edges or margins in the late science text books, for process itself, the provisional and incomplete, are present there also in a variety of forms. Given this duality, this double-sided aspect, it is appropriate to observe, finally, that a central interest of *Deucalion,* the text which has the most to say against Tyndall, should be the glacier – a location, Kate Flint has shown, of a set of discontinuous and competing discourses in the Victorian period[64] and also, importantly for my argument, a body which was imagined as both solid and (seemingly) permanent yet one also seen to be secretly in motion and vulnerable to change. Thus Dorothy Wordsworth, as Flint points out, wrote in 1820, drawing attention to this paradoxical fusion of stasis with movement, that 'no spectacle that I ever beheld – not even the ocean itself – has had an equal power over my mind in bringing together thoughts connected with duration and decay – eternity, and perpetual wasting'.[65] The glacier and glacial movement are not only major topics of *Deucalion* and central locations of Ruskin's most critical words against Tyndall: as an historically recognized site for the coordination of solidity with movement, of change with permanence, the glacier is also a peculiarly appropriate silent presence in this account of Ruskin's relationship with Tyndall, an account which of necessity involved both the detailing of Ruskin's rejection of process and movement in favour of permanence and the durable but also, paradoxically, a description of the very place of process and change within his own late science writing. Like the glacier itself, in other words, Ruskin's rich and multiple argument with Tyndall involves strikingly an indubitable fusion of contraries.

63 *Deucalion: Collected Studies of the Lapse of Waves, and Life of Stones.*
64 Kate Flint, 'Glaciers, Science, and the Imagination', *Textus,* 8 (1995), 43–64.
65 Quoted in Flint, p. 43.

4

'Over yonder are the Andes'

Reading Ruskin reading Humboldt

PAUL WILSON

O N 24 DECEMBER 1836 John Ruskin wrote to his father, regaling him with a jaunty account of a conversation between the new Oxford undergraduate and his old tutor, Revd Thomas Dale. Dale had sternly warned the young Ruskin against taking 'light books' up to Oxford: 'I said something politely implying that his hope would be disappointed – he asked what I called light books – I replied Saussure – Humbolt [sic] – and other works on natural philosophy, geological works, etc, etc.'[1]

Fifty years later, in a letter to Charles Eliot Norton, Ruskin writes: 'By the way, nothing in late reading has delighted me more, or ever did, in praeterite reading, than the letters of aged Humboldt to youthful Agassiz' (37.570). As both bumptious undergraduate and ailing Victorian sage, Ruskin turned to some of the works of Alexander von Humboldt as a source of pleasure, instruction and example. For over half a century Humboldt, along with de Saussure, was to provide Ruskin with a paradigm of exemplary scientific practice, a yardstick against which Ruskin might measure the work of a later generation of nine-teenth-century scientists. Ruskin scholars have frequently noticed the influence of de Saussure's work on Ruskin's development as a writer; Humboldt, how-ever, has been neglected. This has had a somewhat disabling effect on any at-tempt to work towards a proper understanding of Ruskin's scientific writings. Mary Louise Pratt has described Humboldt's work as seeking to head off the bourgeois 'sundering of objectivist and subjectivist strategies, science and sen-timent, information and experience'.[2] Much the same may be said about Ruskin's

1   *The Ruskin Family Letters: The Correspondence of John James Ruskin, his Wife, and their Son, John, 1801–1843*, ed. Van Akin Burd, 2 vols (Ithaca and London: Cornell, 1973), I, 387.

scientific work.

It is perhaps necessary here to give a brief resumé of the career of Humboldt. Born into an aristocratic family on 14 September 1769, Humboldt trained as a mining engineer at Freiburg under the tuition of the leading geologist of his generation, A. G. Werner. Also in his youth he had attended classes at the University of Jena, where he became friendly with Goethe. Goethe's universalist view of a harmonious and interconnected natural world influenced Humboldt's own holistic approach to natural history. Humboldt came to believe that his task was to seek out and uncover the hidden interconnections between all organic and inorganic creation. Before embarking on his five-year journey through equinoctial South America, Humboldt wrote to Karl Freisleben explaining what he expected to achieve on the journey:

> I shall collect plants and fossils and make astronomic observations. But that's not the main purpose of my expedition – I shall try to find out how the forces of nature interact upon one another and how the geographic environment influences plant and animal life. In other words, I must find out about the unity of nature.[3]

Humboldt explored the jungles and mountains of South America during the years 1799–1804, in the company of the botanist Aimé Bonpland. Between them, they amassed an extraordinary wealth of data and specimens, which were to provide the raw material of thirty volumes covering the geography, geology, natural history, spectacular views, and anthropology of the new world, the writing of which occupied Humboldt for much of the next twenty years. Together with these works, he also published his *Personal Narrative of Travels to the Equinoctial Regions of America,* which first appeared in an English translation by Helen Maria Williams between 1814 and 1829. Humboldt's holistic view of the natural world, confirmed and developed by his South American experience, was eventually to result in his *magnum opus, Cosmos* (1845–62), subtitled 'A Sketch of a Physical Description of the Universe'. In the Author's Preface to this colossal work, Humboldt explains that 'the principal impulse' behind all his studies has been 'the earnest endeavour to comprehend the phenomena of physical objects in their general connection, and to represent nature as one great whole, moved and animated by internal forces'.[4]

It is important to recognize just how influential Humboldt's work was dur-

---

2   Mary Louise Pratt, *Imperial Eyes: Travel Writing and Transculturation* (London: Routledge, 1992), p. 119.

3   Alexander von Humboldt, *Personal Narrative of a Journey to the Equinoctial Regions of the New Continent* (Harmondsworth: Penguin, 1995), p. ix.

4   Alexander von Humboldt, *Cosmos* (London: Bohn, 1849), p. ix.

ing the time of Ruskin's apprenticeship as a writer and a scientist. Susan Cannon argues that the first half of the nineteenth century can be seen as the period of 'Humboldtian science', and that 'from about 1800 to about 1840 [Humboldt] successfully directed the attention of many European scientists, especially the younger ones, to a complex of interests'.[5] I want to suggest that Ruskin is amongst these younger scientists in the 1830s, and is particularly receptive of, and responsive to, Humboldt's work.

Before moving on to examine in detail Ruskin's response to Humboldt's writings, it is necessary to try to specify the central features of Humboldtian science. We have already seen that Humboldt's predominant aim is to disclose the harmony of nature. How, in practical terms, is this to be achieved? Firstly, through travel: Humboldtian science is necessarily an excursive activity. Travel allows the scientific observer to compare organic and inorganic formations in a variety of geographic locations, and may enable the observer to attempt to form links between phenomena which are widely distributed over the surface of the planet. Thus, for example, we may find Humboldt likening a cavern in northern Venezuela to Yordas cave in the Yorkshire Dales, or the limestone formations of Derbyshire. Very often, Humboldt will compare mountain forms in the New World to features in the Alps. This must have been exciting and pertinent to the young Ruskin: Humboldt's exotic landscapes are seen to have associations with the landscape features with which he is familiar both through his own juvenile travels and through his knowledge of the Romantic topography of Wordsworth, Byron and Scott.

Also central to the Humboldtian methodology is the close observation of individual phenomena and an avoidance of premature theory. On his geological work in South America, he comments: 'I flatter myself that I may render some service to those geologists who prefer the Knowledge of positive facts to speculation on the origin of things';[6] and later, in the same work: 'These geological questions can be solved only so far as they are directed by the actual state of things, that is of facts susceptible of being verified by observation.'[7] For Humboldt, theory is, in the current state of knowledge, an impertinence. Moreover, there are moments when Humboldt admits to bafflement when faced with certain natural phenomena: however much data is collected, some things

5 Susan Faye Cannon, *Science in Culture: The Early Victorian Period* (New York: Science History, 1978), p. 76.

6 Alexander von Humboldt, *Personal Narrative of Travels to the Equinoctial Regions of America* (London: Bell, 1889), p. 187.

7 Ibid., p. 263.

remain beyond the grasp of understanding. Descending from the volcano of Tenerife, Humboldt muses that 'notwithstanding the care with which we interrogate nature … we return from the summit of a burning volcano less satisfied than when we were preparing to visit it'.[8] This tentativeness and rejection of theoretical speculation was to remain continually attractive to Ruskin throughout his life.

A third feature of Humboldtian science is the importance of measurement. One of Humboldt's legacies to later science was the invention of the 'iso-map', a map indicating lines of equal phenomena. In order to build up these maps, Humboldt, when in the field, was constantly involved in a variety of measurements of temperature, magnetic variation, longitude, elevation, barometric pressure, humidity, the blue of the sky, and so on. The *Personal Narrative* gives countless examples of Humboldt plunging thermometers into mountain streams, stopping to boil water whilst ascending the Andes in order to ascertain how height affects boiling point, getting up at dawn to observe the sunrise, and going without sleep to make observations of the stars.

Cannon lists a number of fields of enquiry which were typical of the Humboldtian scientist of the first half of the nineteenth century: those areas on her list which apply to Ruskin are meteorology, hydrology, the structure of mountain chains, and the orientation of strata. Scientists working in these fields, involved in travel to amass their data through close observation and the measurement of phenomena; who seek to establish interrelationships between those phenomena; and, moreover are keen to mingle empirical observation with subjective response, are Humboldtian: they are, remarks Cannon, 'eagerly participating in the latest wave of international scientific activity'.[9] When Ruskin, at the very beginning of his 1835 diary, records the intensity of the blue of the sky on his cyanometer; when he calculates the amount of debris brought down from the mountains by a typical Alpine stream; and when he scrupulously measures the angles of the summit of the Matterhorn in *Modern Painters* IV (1856), he is very much part of this international, Humboldtian scientific activity.

In February 1835 John James Ruskin bought Helen Maria William's translation of Humboldt's *Personal Narrative*. In June the same year the Ruskins set off on a grand tour of the Alps, which was to result in John's extensive 1835 diary, giving a detailed account of the journey. Critics have remarked upon the influence of Ruskin's early scientific reading on the style and content of the diary – John Dixon Hunt, for example, mentions the influence of de Saussure, the Harry and

8   Ibid., p. 90.
9   Cannon, p. 104.

68

Lucy stories, and Joyce's *Scientific Dialogues*. To this list, it is possible to add the influence of Ruskin's recent reading of the newly-purchased *Personal Narrative*. Wolfgang Kemp has described the 1835 tour as 'an equal blend of science and emotion', and sees in it a dialectical movement between the Alps of Byron and de Saussure.[10] I would add that Ruskin attempts such a synthesis in the 1835 diary having been at least encouraged in this direction by the example of Humboldt. The diary entries shift from precise empirical observation of geological, botanical and meteorological phenomena, to passages of personal response. The 1835 diary may be seen as the early work of an aspiring Humboldtian scientist.

The most clearly Humboldtian work by the young Ruskin is 'Remarks on the Present State of Meteorological Science', first published in the first volume of the *Transactions of the Meteorological Society* in 1839. This was not, however, the first piece he had written for the society. Ruskin had been a member since 1836. In a letter to his father, dated two days after the letter containing the reference to Humboldt quoted at the beginning of this paper, Ruskin remarks that 'I am preparing a superb paper for the Meteorological which will no doubt be put into the Transactions'. In a letter of 10 January 1837, he writes:

> The society would be much better employed, instead of listening to anticipations which will never be realised, and prophecies which the weather takes good care not to fulfil, in ascertaining the causes and effects of phenomena which have actually taken place, or in perusing such scientific and interesting communications as one which I sent to Mr White, and which Richard says will frighten them out of their meteorological wits, containing six close-written folio pages, and having, at its conclusion, the agreeable announcement that it only commences the subject. (1.206)

The paper, according to the Minutes of the Meteorological Society of London, was read by Ruskin on 14 February 1837, and bore the title 'On the formation and colour of such Clouds as are caused by the agency of the Mountains'. Apart from the fact that it was based on the results of observations made by Ruskin in the Alps, nothing further is known about the paper.

There are a number of Humboldtian strands which may be teased out here, the first being the fact of Ruskin's membership of the society itself. Meteorology was then a science in its infancy. The Meteorological Society was not formed until 1823; it published no transactions until the 1839 volume towards which Ruskin contributed his second meteorological paper. The collection of data on climate and meteorological phenomena by the travelling observer was, as

10 Wolfgang Kemp, *The Desire of My Eyes: The Life and Work of John Ruskin* (London: HarperCollins, 1991), p. 48.

Cannon's list shows, one of the marks of the Humboldtian scientist, and such actions figure largely in the *Personal Narrative*. Moreover, meteorological phenomena in connection with the mountains is another vital concern of that work: the very title of Ruskin's earlier paper hints at Humboldt's influence. So too does the meteorological position adopted by Ruskin in the January letter. He rejects the view which sees meteorology as primarily a predictive science, and insists instead on the observation and recording of 'the causes and effects of phenomena which have actually taken place'. Moreover, Ruskin wants to stress that there is much work still to be done: his suggestions merely mark the commencement of the subject, and the implication is that the time for speculation and theory has not yet arrived. It is difficult not to be reminded of Humboldt's resistance to speculation and his insistence on concentrating on 'the actual state of things', and 'facts susceptible of being verified by observation'.

Ruskin's 'Remarks on the Present State of Meteorological Science', the second article in the first *Transactions* of the Meteorological Society, can be seen as a manifesto for this young, avant-garde, cosmopolitan science. Ruskin seeks to vindicate meteorology and claim for it 'an equal position among the proud thrones of its sister sciences' (1.207). He denies that meteorology is a field of inquiry occupied by the dilettante: he does not 'bring meteorology forward as a pursuit adapted for the occupation of tedious leisure, or the amusement of a careless hour'. Instead, he regards his audience as 'men of science and learning'. He also denies that meteorology should be studied primarily because it is a subject which possesses beauty 'in no ordinary degree'. However, while denying beauty as a reason for study, Ruskin simultaneously rhapsodizes over the aesthetic and ethical value of the science. He draws a stark contrast between the meteorologist's field of enquiry and that of the labourer within the 'deathful laboratory', and the 'charnel-houses of creation'. It is remarkable to see Ruskin describing laboratory practices in these Frankensteinian terms here, half a century before he was to resign his Professorship over the proposal to introduce vivisection to Oxford's own 'deathful laboratories'. The dualistic pattern of much of the older Ruskin's thinking is here already evident: the 'gaseous exhalations' of the dissecting room and the 'pure air' of meteorology are structurally identical with the polarity of the hideous sloth and the divine squirrel of 'Yewdale and its Streamlets' (1878).

But, pre-eminently beautiful though the study of meteorology may be, Ruskin asserts that the proper justification of the science must be its ultimate utility. Given that what Ruskin is writing here is, as I have described it, a manifesto for the work of the Meteorological Society, this move is well judged. For besides his assimilation of the lessons of the Humboldtian methodology, it indicates that he is also in tune with the utilitarian natural thelogy which was crucial to the ideology of the physical sciences in England in the late 1830s: particularly, and almost exactly contemporaneously, with the drift of the work of his mentor, Revd Dr William Buckland of Christ Church, who was arguing that geology was justified on the grounds that it was able to uncover England's God-given coal reserves.

A digression is necessary here into the work of Humboldt himself which was contemporaneous with Ruskin's membership of the Meteorological Society. Besides his invention of the iso-map, one of Humboldt's greatest practical achievements was the setting up of an international network to measure the magnetic field of the planet. In 1836 he had written to the Duke of Sussex, then President of the Royal Society, to put forward the idea of permanent stations for the observation and measurement of magnetic variations throughout the territory of the British empire. In 1839, on the recommendation of both the Royal Society and the British Association, the government gave approval to the setting up of geomagnetic stations across the globe in accordance with Humboldt's principles.

In his meteorological paper, Ruskin reinforces his adoption of a Humboldtian stance by advocating a similar system of global observation and measurement within the science of meteorology. Advances can only be made in the fledgling science through co-operative global action. Ruskin asserts that 'the meteorologist is impotent if alone ... no progress can be made by the enthusiasm of an individual' (1.209). The paper concludes with a call for planetary co-operation and the pooling of data in order to understand the fundamental laws of meteorology. Ruskin's vision of the future of the science is remarkable. He sees a planet-wide system of observers:

> Let the pastor of the Alps observe the variations of his mountain winds; let the voyagers send us notes of their changes on the surface of the sea; let the solitary dweller in the American prairie observe the passages of the storms, and the variations of the climate ... (1.210)

The observational data will be conveyed back to the Meteorological Society which will thereby become 'one mighty Mind ... one vast Eye ... a multitudinous Power' (1.210). Thus will 'the most deeply hidden problems of Nature' be solved, and, in true Humboldtian fashion, the underlying unity of Nature revealed: we will uncover the 'principle and order' which lies behind 'the vast multitude of beautiful and wonderful phenomena'. So far, so Humboldtian. But Ruskin ends the paper on a note which we do not associate with Humboldtian science. For while Humboldt's approach is thoroughly holistic, any reading of his work will soon convince the reader that Humboldt is by no means a natural theologian. God is conspicuously absent from both the *Personal Narrative* and *Cosmos*. This quiet refusal on Humboldt's part to ascribe the unity he finds in nature to the working of Divine providence causes difficulties for Ruskin when he eventually encounters *Cosmos* in the late 1840s, as I examine below. Here, in the final sentence of 'Remarks on the Present State of Meteorological Science', Ruskin yokes Humboldtian method with natural theology. The global collection of data does more than uncover the 'principle and order' of nature: it allows us to understand how 'the wisdom and benevolence of the Supreme Deity regulates the course of the times and the seasons, robes the globe with verdure and fruitfulness, and adapts it to minister to the wants, and contribute to the felicity, of the innumerable tribes of animated existence' (1.210).

Whilst 'Remarks on the Present state of Meteorological Science' suggests the influence of Humboldt on the undergraduate of Oxford, it is not until Volume III of *Modern Painters* (1856) that Ruskin mentions his work in print: and then he does so in a problematic and puzzling way.

In the Appendix on 'Plagiarism' in *Modern Painters* III Ruskin appears to deny the influence of Humboldt on his own work:

> Many people will suppose that for several ideas in the chapter on landscape I was indebted to Humboldt's *Kosmos* ... Of Humboldt's *Kosmos* I heard much talk when it first came out, and looked through it cursorily: but thinking it contained no material (connected with my subject) which I had not already possessed myself of, I have never since referred to the work. I may be mistaken in my estimate of it, but certainly owe it absolutely nothing. (5.428)

The reasons behind this denial of Humboldt need to be carefully investigated.

To begin with, it must be noted that Ruskin refers specifically to *Cosmos* here. *Cosmos* began to appear in an English translation from 1846 onwards. It appears that Ruskin had read some of this in 1847. The second volume contains an investigation of different cultural representations of the natural world: Chapter I of Part I focuses on 'Descriptions of Nature by the ancients; Descriptions of Nature by the Greeks; Descriptions of Nature by the Romans ...', and so on, through the Persians and Hebrews, to Columbus, Camoens, and, finally, Goethe. Chapter II examines 'Landscape painting, in its influence on the study of nature'. Clearly, Ruskin's and Humboldt's interests converge once again: however, there is little if any overlap in the substance of the second volume of *Cosmos* and the landscape chapters of *Modern Painters* III. Whereas Ruskin focuses his attention in each of Chapters XIII–XVI around individual figures – Homer,

Dante, and Scott – taking each of them as representative of the historical and cultural consciousness of their times, Humboldt ranges more widely. His chapter on Greek descriptions of nature mentions Homer alongside Hesiod, Empedocles, Pindar, Sophocles, Euripedes and the Greek Anthology, among others. Humboldt's survey is wider in scope, but somewhat cursory, lacking in the imaginative penetration of Ruskin's chapters. Why then did Ruskin feel he had to distance himself from Humboldt in *Modern Painters* III?

There are a number of factors which need to be mentioned. It is important to recognize that *Cosmos* is a very different text from the *Personal Narrative*. Humboldt no longer writes within the discursive field of scientific travel, which is so important and influential for Ruskin's own work. Instead of a vast chain of close descriptions of a multiplicity of disparate natural phenomena linked by the narrative eye of the observer Humboldt, *Cosmos* represents an attempt to see interconnections within the natural world from some imaginary space beyond it. Humboldt declares that his aim is 'to represent nature as one great whole moved and animated by internal forces'; *Cosmos* will 'embrace a summary of physical knowledge, as connected with a delineation of the material universe'.[11] Without the controlling narrative of the earlier work, which stresses the power and intensity of the narrator's observations of the facticity of the world through which he travels, *Cosmos* threatens to collapse into a massive compendium of data, a vast 'summary' in place of a narrative of discovery. Moreover, Humboldt's reference to 'internal forces' here is deeply problematic for Ruskin. As mentioned above, Humboldt is no natural theologian, a fact which is more apparent in this huge 'summary' than in his narrative. I will return to this point in a moment.

The evidence seems to suggest that both Pauline Trevelyan and Henry Acland were worried about Ruskin's readers making a connection between *Modern Painters* III and *Cosmos*. In a letter to Pauline Trevelyan, dated Christmas 1855 – the period immediately before the publication of *Modern Painters* III – Ruskin writes:

> I did as I was bid – about Humboldt but here – by your Agency & Acland, is the world deprived of an important fact. That *was* the fact Kosmos did verily appear to me – at that period of my life – I may have been wrong or right – but so it was, and now there is this Absolute Fact for ever lost & extinguished under a Phrase, and so few facts as one can ever get at! too![12]

It is hardly surprising that the editor of this correspondence remarks of this

---

11 Humboldt (1849), p. ix and p. vii.

12 *Reflections of a Friendship: John Ruskin's Letters to Pauline Trevelyan 1848–1866*, ed. Virginia Surtees (London: Allen, Unwin, 1979), pp. 108–9.

tortuous passage that 'this paragraph is unexplained'. But I believe that it is at least possible to propose an explanation once we understand that Ruskin is referring here to Appendix II of *Modern Painters* III.

I want to suggest that Ruskin, under pressure from his friends, seeks to distance himself from the influence of Humboldt on religious grounds. It is likely that he was already aware of Carlyle's disapproval of *Cosmos*. In 1857, Carlyle was to condemn the work precisely because of Humboldt's vision of a unified nature 'animated by internal forces'. Carlyle complained that the 'spiritual world, and all spiritual life [was] quite ignored'. He went on: 'The higher and nobler side of man's existence not even hinted at – a lamentable picture, truly'.[13] Ruskin seems to have accepted Carlyle's estimate of *Cosmos*, as later references demonstrate. In a letter to the children of Winnington Hall, written sometime in 1860, Ruskin uses Carlyle to warn the girls away from Humboldt's *magnum opus*:

> To prevent any of you from being ever beguiled into reading Humboldt's Kosmos reverentially – I may tell you that Carlyle after expressing the greatest delight in, & sympathy with, de Saussure, showing that he (Carlyle) entirely felt what a naturalist ought to be; he burst out into a noble declamation of evidently well grounded contempt for Humboldt – and for the Kosmos especially – terminating it by saying that Humboldt was "no better than the old Fountain by Edinburgh Tolbooth – with swollen leaded cheeks and a brass pipe in the mouth of it".[14]

A second account of the same conversation shows Ruskin approvingly taking up Carlyle's condemnation of Humboldt's brazen excesses: 'This mightily pleased me who always considered Kosmos the impudentest thing ever yet done by dull human brass'.[15]

It must be re-emphasized at this point that the work which is continually attacked in this barrage of criticism is *Cosmos*: the *Personal Narrative* is not mentioned. For Ruskin, when Humboldt ceased to be a writer of scientific travels and embarked on *Cosmos*, it was as if he had evolved into one of those hubristic men of science who induce so much of Ruskin's bile from mid-century onwards. Humboldt's universe has no need of Divine guidance, and in *Modern Painters* III, Ruskin denies Humboldtian influence in order that his audience will not infer, from a similarity of interest, that Ruskin might covertly share Humboldt's view of a natural order regulated purely by 'internal forces'. Ruskin puts clear water between himself and Humboldt, just as, and for similar reasons,

13 *The Winnington Letters: John Ruskin's Correspondence with Margaret Alexis Bell and the Children of Winnington Hall*, ed. Van Akin Burd (London: Allen, Unwin, 1969), p. 228n.

14 Ibid., p. 227.

15 Surtees, p. 161.

in the same Appendix he denies any influence on his own work on the part of Pugin.

But what of the 'Absolute Fact' referred to in the opaque note to Pauline Trevelyan? Ruskin's obvious unease here seems to indicate fairly clearly that he is not happy about being manoeuvred into a position where he is seen to be dismissing Humboldt's work *tout court*. His dismissal of Humboldt's influence on *Modern Painters* is surely economical with the truth. For the Humboldt of the *Personal Narrative* has been both inspirational and a model for some of Ruskin's work up to this point, and will continue to function as such later. Here, I suggest, is the 'Absolute Fact': Humboldt the scientific traveller was, and remains, a paradigmatic figure in the Ruskinian project.

However, although there is a brief reference to an episode in the *Personal Narrative* in *Modern Painters* V (1860), it is not until he is engaged upon the scientific work of the 1870s that Ruskin begins to promote publicly Humboldt as the exemplary scientist of the first part of the nineteenth century. References to the *Personal Narrative* begin in 1873, in both *Fors Clavigera* (1871–84) and *Love's Meinie* (1873). In the second lecture on birds, delivered at Oxford on 2 May 1873, Ruskin refers to and quotes from Humboldt's description of the nocturnal birds which inhabit the cave of Caripe in northern Venezuela. The tone of this passage is relaxed; Ruskin makes mild fun of Humboldt's difficulties in classifying the nocturnal birds. But this simply serves as an introduction to Ruskin's equally bizarre classification: 'Well, Humboldt is reduced, by necessities of recent classification, to call a bird three and a half feet across the wings, a sparrow. I have no right to laugh at him, for I am just going, myself, to call the cheerfullest and brightest of birds of the air, an owl' (25.54). Significantly, this genial passage comes only a page or two before an angry assault on an extract from Darwin's *Descent of Man* (1871). Again in 1873, Ruskin quotes Humboldt's account of the diet of the Otomac Indians in Letter 27 of *Fors*: this becomes a platform for a diatribe on contemporary English economics.

Ruskin continues to read the *Personal Narrative* throughout the 1870s. A diary entry from 1876 records: 'The sunset almost too bright *through* the blind for me to read Humboldt at tea by.'[16] Contemporaneous with this entry, approving references to the Humboldt of the *Personal Narrative* can be found in *Deucalion* (1875–83) and *The Laws of Fésole* (1877–78). In *Deucalion*, Humboldt, together with de Saussure, is designated as one of 'the most careful and logical geologists'

16 Helen Gill Viljoen, *The Brantwood Diary of John Ruskin, together with selected related letters and sketches of persons mentioned* (New Haven and London: Yale University Press, 1971), p. 19.

(26.281). Later in the same work, Ruskin recruits the writer of the *Personal Narrative* as an example of a natural theologian: 'in the earlier and happier days of Linnaeus, de Saussure, von Humboldt and the multitude of quiet workers on whose secure foundation the fantastic expiations of modern science depend for whatever good or stability there is in them, natural religion was always a part of natural science' (26.339). This is mere sleight-of-hand on Ruskin's part, but a further *Deucalion* reference distinguishes between the religious Linnaeus and the rather different but still vital qualities which Ruskin values in Humboldt: 'The nobly religious passion in which Linnaeus writes the prefaces and summaries of the *Systema Naturae*, with the universal and serene philanthropy and sagacity of Humboldt, agree in leading them to the optimist conclusion, best and unsurpassably expressed for ever in Pope's *Essay on Man*' (26.343). Here Humboldt is not claimed as an upholder of natural religion, but is praised for his serenity and wisdom, which lead to the optimistic conclusion that, in nature, whatever is, is right. It is not unlikely that the serenity of the *Personal Narrative* comes to be particularly valued by Ruskin in the mid 1870s, when the serenity and optimism of his own philosophy are rapidly disintegrating.

The most extensive reference to Humboldt comes at the end of the fifth chapter of *The Laws of Fésole*. The chapter is entitled 'Of Elementary Form', and after a series of exercises in the arrangement of circular forms into symmetrical and asymmetrical patterns, Ruskin considers human responses to the patterns of the stars. This leads him into a lengthy quotation from the *Personal Narrative*, recounting Humboldt's first sight of the Southern Cross, which closes the chapter. The passage deserves to be quoted in full:

> "We saw distinctly for the first time the Cross of the South only, in the night of the 4th and 5th of July, in the sixteenth degree of latitude; it was strongly inclined, and appeared from time to time between the clouds, the centre of which, furrowed by uncondensed lightnings, reflected a silver light."
>
> *If a traveller may be permitted to speak of his personal emotions,* I shall add, that in this night I saw one of the reveries of my earliest youth accomplished.
>
> "At a period when I studied the heavens, *not with the intention of devoting myself to astronomy*, but only to acquire a *knowledge of the stars*, I was agitated by a fear unknown to those who love a sedentary life. It seemed painful to me to renounce the hope of beholding those beautiful constellations which border the southern pole. Impatient to rove in the equinoctial regions, I could not raise my eyes towards the starry vault without thinking of the Cross of the South, and without recalling the sublime passage of Dante, which the most celebrated commentators have applied to this constellation:

"Io mi voesi a man destra, e posi mente
  All' altro polo, e vidi quattro stelle
  Non viste mai, fuor ch'alla prima gente,
Goder paresa, 'I ciel di lor fiamelle.
  O settentrional vedovo sito,
  Poi che privato se' di mirar quelle!"

"The two great stars which mark the summit and the foot of the Cross having
nearly the same right ascension, it follows hence that the constellation is almost
perpendicular at the moment when it passes the meridian. This circumstance is known
to every nation that lives beyond the tropics or in the southern hemisphere. It has
been observed at what hour of the night, in different seasons, the Cross of the
South is erect, or inclined. It is a timepiece that advances very regularly near four
minutes a day; and no other group of stars exhibits, to the naked eye, an observation
of time so easily made. How often have we heard our guides exclaim, in the savannahs
of the Venezuela, or in the desert extending from Lima to Truxillo, 'Midnight is
past, the Cross begins to bend!' How often those words reminded us of that affecting
scene where Paul and Virginia, seated near the source of the river of Lataniers,
conversed together for the last time, and where the old man, at the sight of the
Southern Cross, warns them that it is time to separate!"
(15.393–94) (*Ruskin's emphases*)

This 'beautiful passage', as Ruskin calls it, can provide significant insights into
his philosophy of science in the 1870s. One of the things which is most striking about this passage is just how Ruskinian it seems, particularly in its associative movement from the contemplation of natural phenomena to the human
domain. It would not be difficult – indeed, one would almost expect – a reverie
centred on the constellation of the Southern Cross to dwell on otherness, re-
moteness, the distance from Eurocentric 'civilised' values. This is, indeed, exactly what the Dante quotation does, speaking of 'that alien pole', seen once by
'the first men, and since, no living eye'. But Humboldt's imagination humanizes
the Southern Cross through association – with his childhood longings, memories of his South American travels, and recollections of aesthetic experience.
For Humboldt, the Southern Cross is not alien: even as a child, the yet unseen
phenomenon was already pre-inscribed for him with aesthetic significance because of his reading of the *Purgatorio*. On further acquaintance with the actual
phenomenon of the rising and setting of the constellation, further humanizing
associations accrue: the stars have a function as a timepiece within the world of
the human. And the passage ends with the Southern Cross again embedded
within a familiar text, further loaded with human significance by its appearance
in *Paul and Virginia*. Thus, for Humboldt, the Southern Cross becomes surrounded
by a secondary constellation of associations which fix it as part of the world of

human signification.

Humboldt's articulation here of the power of the pre-inscription of a natural phenomenon such as the Southern Cross to convey human value and meaning is very close to Ruskin's own position. Elsewhere, Humboldt points out that, for the European observer, the landscape of the New World may lack the affective qualities of a European landscape which is always already inscribed with deep historical associations. Thus, in the introduction to the *Personal Narrative*, Humboldt writes:

> In the Old World, nations and the distinctions of their civilisations form the principal points in the picture; in the New World, man and his productions almost disappear amidst the stupendous display of wild and gigantic nature. The human race in the New World presents only a few remnants of indigenous hordes, slightly advanced in civilisation; or it exhibits merely the uniformity of manners and institutions transplanted by European colonists to foreign shores. Information which relates to the history of our species, to the various forms of government, to monuments of art, to places full of great remembrances, affect us far more than descriptions of those vast solitudes which seem destined only for the development of vegetable life, and to be the domain of wild animals.[17]

This passage is suggestively reminiscent of the well-known description of the landscape of the Jura which opens 'The Lamp of Memory'. Ruskin's contrast of this landscape with 'some aboriginal forest of the New Continent' (8.223) is very close to Humboldt. The pine forest above Champagnole becomes 'oppressively desolate' once it is imaginatively deprived of what Humboldt terms the 'great remembrances' of 'the history of our species'.

In the second of the two passages which Ruskin emphasizes in his extract, he points up the distinction between 'a knowledge of the stars' and 'astronomy'. The first, he tells us in a foot-note, is 'modestly useful'; the second 'vainly ambitious'. This seems to distinguish neatly between the 'good' Humboldt of the *Personal Narrative*, and the 'bad' Humboldt of *Cosmos*. But there are further implications, for one of the main lines of attack on men of science in this later period of Ruskin's life is precisely that they are 'vainly ambitious' in a number of ways. They are both vain and ambitious in their desire for personal glory; Ruskin castigates John Tyndall in particular for his seeming desire to be recognized for his discoveries. But they also stand accused of vain ambition in the sense that they strive for knowledge which is beyond the boundaries of human use. Astronomy is one such science, amassing knowledge which, for Ruskin, has no value within the human domain, and, more dangerously, tempting the scien-

17 Humboldt (1889), p. xxi.

tist into the realms of the infinite. But 'knowledge of the stars' is grounded in the human and operates within the parameters of the human niche. It is, firstly, useful: just as the young Ruskin defended meteorology on the grounds of utility, so the much older Ruskin defends the study of the stars provided it has some human use. For Humboldt, the stars are both navigational aid and timepiece: a knowledge of them is therefore valid and praiseworthy, as far as Ruskin is concerned. Furthermore, knowledge of the stars can be seen to have an aesthetic dimension, not simply in terms of an appreciation of their beauty, but also an awareness of their role in art. The stars gain in aesthetic significance if we know how they figure in the writings of Dante and St Pierre.

Ruskin adds a foot-note to the end of the first passage which he emphasizes in his extract, which explains that: 'I italicise, because the reserve of the *Personal Narrative*, in this respect, is almost majestic; and entirely exemplary as compared with the explosive egotism of the modern tourist'. The 'modern tourist' whom Ruskin most has in mind here is likely to be John Tyndall, whose book of scientific travel *The Glaciers of the Alps* (1860) is castigated in *Deucalion*. Egotism is a further element in Ruskin's catalogue of criticism of contemporary science. Phenomena of nature are overshadowed by the vanity and self-regard of the scientist, according to the Ruskinian critique: in comparison, the Humboldt of the *Personal Narrative* exhibits an exemplary reserve. Humility, then, together with a concern for utility, an aesthetic understanding, and a determination to locate knowledge firmly within the boundaries of the human niche, are the characteristics of the exemplary scientist for the Ruskin of the 1870s.

Humboldt continues to figure as such an exemplar throughout the next decade as well. In 1881 Ruskin writes to the Revd J. P. Faunthorpe: 'I am going to try to get for Miss Kemm Humboldt and Bonpland's *Mimosas* – a miracle of quiet tenderness and perfect art, without a shadow of vanity, insolence, or vulgar investigation' (37.380). (The reference is to *Mimoses et autres plantes légumineuses de Nouveau Continent*, published in 1819 as Part VI of Humboldt and Bonpland's massive documentary record of their South American journey.) Towards the end of the decade, Ruskin became involved in public correspondence with reference to Sir John Lubbock's list of the world's best hundred books. Ruskin declares that: 'Of travels I read myself all old ones I can get hold of; of modern, Humboldt is the central model' (34.583). A little later, he writes: 'I never read English sermons or scientific books, and only Humboldt (translated) of German' (34.606).

I want to suggest that the fact of Ruskin's continual engagement with the *Personal Narrative* in the 1870s and 1880s can help in the interpretation of a curious passage from the second instalment of *Fiction, Fair and Foul* (1880). This work marks the culmination of Ruskin's disengagement from Wordsworth, a process which began nearly twenty-five years earlier in *Modern Painters* III. Part of Ruskin's dissatisfaction with Wordsworth derives, as Elizabeth Helsinger has argued, from Wordsworth's failure to understand the value of the observational strategies of the natural scientist. Helsinger writes that, for Ruskin:

> Wordsworth ... does not appreciate the importance of natural science ... . The observations of the natural scientist, like the slow progress of the traveller, can be another route to fuller perception. In place of the quick grasp of imaginative perception, the scientist labors to assemble perceptual data that will multiply the significance of the experience. The natural scientist also can discover, as Ruskin elsewhere writes, "the inner relations of all these things to the universe, and to man" and learn to perceive undreamt-of "natural energies" and "past states of being". [18]

The natural scientist delineated here seems particularly Humboldtian: the gradual assemblage of data through travel, which then leads on to the discovery of occult links within the world of natural phenomena, is the method of the *Personal Narrative*. And I would argue that it is the case that, in the second part of *Fiction, Fair and Foul*, Ruskin privileges the Humboldtian observer over the Lakeland poet. The passage in question begins by referring to Matthew Arnold's edition of Wordsworth:

> I have lately seen, and with extreme pleasure, Mr. Matthew Arnold's arrangement of Wordsworth's poems; and read with sincere interest his high estimate of them. But a great poet's work never needs arrangement by other hands; and though it is very proper that Silver How should clearly understand and brightly praise its fraternal Rydal Mount, we must not forget that, over yonder, are the Andes, all the while. (34.318)

Ruskin here diminishes the standing of both Arnold and Wordsworth: he is leading to the devastating conclusion in the next paragraph but one that 'Wordsworth is simply a Lakeland peasant'. This is achieved by translating Arnold and Wordsworth into topographic features. Arnold becomes Silver How: an error on Ruskin's part, for it is likely that he meant Fox How, the Arnold family home near Ambleside. Yet it is a creative mistake, for Silver How is, as Ruskin knew, the small bracken-covered fell which overlooks the classic Wordworthian topos of Grasmere: similarly, Arnold seeks to overlook/oversee the genuine territory of Wordsworth. The lowly Rydal Mount and Silver How are set over

---

18 Elizabeth K. Helsinger, *Ruskin and the Art of the Beholder* (Cambridge, Mass. and London: Harvard University Press, 1982), p. 65.

against the soaring peaks of the Andes, emphasizing the relative littleness and lack of grandeur of the Lakeland topography. The Lakeland landscape remains beloved, of course, but Ruskin suggests that true sublimity lies elsewhere.

The reference to the Andes surely must strike the reader at first as eccentric: normally, one would expect Ruskin to use the Alps as his symbol of greatness. The reference only begins to make sense once we understand that, as Arnold and Wordsworth become topography, so the figure of Humboldt lies behind the evocation of the Andes. Ruskin's knowledge of the Andes derives from his reading of Humboldt: Chapter XXXII of the *Personal Narrative* is an extensive account of the geography and geology of the South American mountains. Thus, besides the texts of Arnold's edition of Wordsworth, and Wordsworth's poems themselves, a third work is quietly evoked in this passage, and is elevated above them: the *Personal Narrative* of Alexander von Humboldt.

There are some interesting implications if my reading of this passage is accepted. For, whilst *Fiction, Fair and Foul* plainly seeks to demote Wordsworth as a poet once and for all in favour of Byron, we may now see that Wordsworth as observer of natural phenomena is similarly demoted in favour of Humboldt. The towering Andean figure of Humboldt serves as a final sign of Ruskin's estimation of Wordsworth's 'narrowness of mind': a narrowness which as far back as *Modern Painters* III is seen as closely connected with Wordsworth's incapacity for a true understanding of the value of natural science: 'This was the chief narrowness of Wordsworth's mind; he could not understand that to break a rock with a hammer in search of crystal may sometimes be an act not disgraceful to human nature, and that to dissect a flower may sometimes be as proper as to dream over it'(5.359). Furthermore, Wordsworth is seen to exhibit those qualities of egotistical self-regard which Ruskin condemns in contemporary men of science: the poet displays 'a vague notion that nature would not be able to get on well without Wordsworth; and finds a considerable part of his pleasure in looking at himself as well as at her' (5.343). Ruskin's idealized version of the Humboldt of the *Personal Narrative* is, by contrast, serene, humble, and without vanity. For the Ruskin of the 1880s, then, the Romantic poet of nature is firmly demoted in favour of the Romantic natural scientist.

Ruskin's final reference to Humboldt comes as late as 1886, in a letter to Charles Eliot Norton. And here Ruskin at last shifts his attention away from the *Personal Narrative*, and is moved by some late texts produced by the elderly Humboldt. 'By the way', Ruskin writes to Norton, 'nothing in late reading has delighted me more, or ever did, in præterite reading, than the letters of aged Humboldt to youthful Agassiz' (37.570). These letters appeared in *Louis Agassiz:*

His Life and Correspondence, edited by his wife Elizabeth, and first published in 1885. It is at first sight odd that Ruskin should be reading this book, given his contemptuous dismissal of Agassiz's work in *Præterita* (1885–89). In his recollection of his six week period of convalescence at Dr Jephson's in Leamington in 1841, Ruskin describes how he bought a copy of Agassiz's *Poissons Fossiles* and set himself to 'counting of scales and learning of hard names, – thinking, as some people do still, that in that manner I might best advance in geology' (35.301). However, Ruskin was eventually to come to the conclusion that Agassiz 'was a mere blockhead to have paid for all that good drawing of the nasty ugly things, and that it didn't matter a stale herring to any mortal whether they had any names or not'. It is possible that Ruskin was attracted to the *Poissons Fossiles* because of the connection between the work and Humboldt. The young Agassiz was something of a protégé of Humboldt's, and the *Poissons Fossiles* was in fact dedicated to the elder naturalist as a tribute to his assistance, financial and intellectual, in the writing of the book. It does not seem unlikely that the fact of this dedication attracted Ruskin to the work and encouraged him to invest so much time in its study.

If the dedication to Humboldt attracted the young Ruskin to Agassiz's influential study of prehistoric fish, so too did the presence of Humboldt's letters draw the elderly Ruskin to Agassiz's *Life and Correspondence.* Humboldt's letters indicate an affectionate, paternal concern on the part of the elder naturalist. He writes warmly in praise of Agassiz's work, worries that he may on occasion take on too much, shows concern when it appears that Agassiz is being side-tracked from the work which Humboldt considers to be of most import (ironically, it is the completion of *Poissons Fossiles* which most often exercises Humboldt's concern). The very nature of this relationship is significant. It is exactly the kind of relationship which Ruskin himself had sought with a younger man of science since at least the late 1860s. In 1869, for example, Ruskin wrote to John Tyndall, enclosing a copy of *The Queen of the Air* (1869). This kindly letter – the tone is remarkable considering Ruskin's later vituperation of Tyndall's work – offers an invitation for Tyndall to join Ruskin in some unspecified future work: 'I shall hope ... that you will stay more within reach of us all and perhaps help me a little in some plans'.[19] In the 1870s Ruskin cajoles and encourages the Lakeland geologist James Clifton Ward into assisting him with parts of *Deucalion.* And in the 1880s he strikes up a similar relationship with the physicist Oliver Lodge.

19 A. S. Eve and C. H. Creasey, *The Life and Work of John Tyndall* (London: Macmillan, 1945), p. 138.

Once again, then, Humboldt's example confirms Ruskin's own practice. Moreover, Humboldt's letters carry a heavy freight of pedagogical authority: Humboldt actively seeks to steer Agassiz in a particular direction, and, most importantly, away from the wilder shores of speculative theory. We have already seen how, in the *Personal Narrative*, Humboldt resists speculation in favour of the collection of data and minute observation of natural phenomena. This remains the position in the letters to Agassiz. In particular, Humboldt continued to resist Agassiz's major contribution to environmental science – the postulation of a European Ice Age. And, in a letter dated 2 March 1842, Humboldt gives a clear statement of his position with regard to geological theory: 'I am inclined, perhaps wrongly, to see all geological theories as having their origin in a mythical region, where, along with the problems of physics, these visions are modified from century to century.'[20] Theories are culturally driven, and are therefore mutable: the real task of the natural scientist is patient observation – a position which accords very closely indeed with that of Ruskin.

My argument has been that, from 1835 to the close of Ruskin's active life, Humboldt's work – with the large exception of *Cosmos* – is a source of inspiration. Humboldt is the paradigmatic natural scientist – humble; patient; hardworking; dedicated to the accurate transcription of his experience of natural phenomena. Moreover, the method of Humboldt's translation of observation into text provides a model for Ruskin's own work. For Humboldt is not merely inscribing raw data drawn from his observations: the results of his seeing are incorporated within a 'personal narrative', a sequential telling in which both observer and observed have weight and value. In telling his scientific findings within the structure of a 'personal narrative', Humboldt intentionally blurs the space between subjective and objective. Moreover, the narrative itself replicates the kind of interconnectedness which Humboldt finds deeply structured within the natural world: the personal narrative is a kind of ecological telling, in which all parts are related to the whole. The affective and associative powers of natural phenomena are also allowed to be articulated within Humboldt's narrative, but without betraying Humboldt into the pathetic fallacy. And the concentration on personal observation disposes Humboldt to resist speculative theory as fundamentally of little value; theory, being culturally driven, is mutable, a kind of writing in sand. Only observation in the realm of the experiential is concrete enough to have value and meaning for dwellers within the human niche. Thus, through his practice as scientist, traveller, observer, and mentor, Humboldt draws

20 *Louis Agassiz: sa Vie et sa Corréspondence*, ed. Elizabeth Agassiz (Paris: Fischbacher, 1887), p. 274.

from Ruskin that sincerest form of flattery, imitation. From the 1835 diary through to the very last works, Ruskin can be seen, in some respects, to be composing his own 'personal narrative'.

5

Was Ruskin a Materialist?

CLIVE WILMER

ACCORDING TO the Oxford English Dictionary, the word 'materialism' has three senses. The third of these is archaic and has no bearing on the present discussion, but the other two will need to be considered before I can broach my theme. The first is philosophical:

> The opinion that nothing exists except matter and its movements and modifications; also, in a more limited sense, the opinion that the phenomena of consciousness and will are wholly due to the operation of material agencies. Often applied by opponents to views that are considered logically to lead to these conclusions, or to involve the attribution to material causes of effects that should be referred to spiritual causes. (OED. 1)

This is worth keeping in mind, though I doubt if we could find room for Ruskin within its terms. The second sense is subdivided into three 'transferred uses', which include the most obvious popular usage of the word:

(a) Applied in reproach to theological views ... that are supposed to imply a defective sense of the reality of things purely spiritual.
(b) In art, the tendency to lay stress on the material aspect of the objects represented.
(c) Devotion to material needs or desires, to the neglect of spiritual matters; a way of life, opinion, or tendency based entirely upon material interests. (OED. 2)

Subdivision 'c' is plainly inapplicable to Ruskin, though it is perhaps worth mentioning that it comes close in meaning to one of his most frequent terms of reproach, namely 'sensualism'. [1] The other subdivisions, though also inapplicable in the end, are not wholly irrelevant to Ruskin's thought. There can be no doubt that Ruskin does stress 'the material aspect' of art, though that is far from being the end of the story. The OED citations include, in this context, a quotation from a book with which Ruskin was familiar, Mrs Jameson's *Legends of the Madonna* (1857): 'The grand materialism of Michael Angelo is supposed to have been allied to the genius of Dante.' One can *just* imagine the newly 'unconverted' Ruskin praising Veronese's *Solomon and Sheba* (as in Chapter 1 of *Præterita* vol. III) for its noble materialism – though the word and its derivatives are rare in his writings and, when they do occur, tend to be used in the most conventionally pejorative of modern senses, as when in *Modern Painters* V he denounces 'the faithless and materialised mind of modern Europe' (7.327). As for the theological category of subdivision 'a', it could – with a little forcing – be made to resemble something in the 'unconverted' Ruskin; the side of him that leans towards the social gospel.

But no, if I had been wanting to prove that Ruskin was, in spite of appearances, a materialist, I would effectively have fallen at the first fence. Ruskin, after all, was essentially a Christian, even after his 'unconversion', and the only philosopher he cites to any large extent is Plato, than whom no thinker could be less materialistic. In 1861, when he was working on *Munera Pulveris*, Ruskin began a serious study of Plato – especially of *The Laws* – which he was to pursue for most of the rest of his life; certainly, between 1876 and 1880, he read a passage from Plato every day (24.xliv). So there would seem to be a case for thinking of Ruskin as in some sense a Platonist and an idealist.[2]

And yet isn't he constantly attacking idealism – or idealisation at any rate? So much of what he values is located in particulars: why else would he attend so closely to the variety of capitals in medieval buildings or devote so much time as a draughtsman to specific instances of natural beauty – a holly-sprig, a mineral vein, a cockleshell? What he cares about, surely, is this-worldly.[3] We have here, perhaps, an example of the self-contradiction Ruskin 'gloried in' (5.liv),

---

1   Inevitably the words 'sensualism' and 'sensualist' to some extent evoke the voluptuous. In his use of them, however, Ruskin always seems to imply something beyond mere venial sensuality. His 'sensualism' is antithetical to both the spiritual and the morally good – e.g. 'Others have a tendency to choose the evil and leave the good, whom, for convenience' sake, I termed Sensualists' (5.103).

2   An important objection to this line of argument has been made by Catherine Williams in her pamphlet *Ruskin's Philosophy* (Penzance: Triton, 1975). This was originally Chapter X of her PhD thesis: *Ruskin's Late Works c. 1870–90, with particular reference to the collection, made for the Guild of St George, the St George's Museum, established at Sheffield, 1875–1953, and now kept at Reading University*, PhD thesis submitted to the University of London, 1972. I am grateful to Dinah Birch for drawing my attention to Williams's work, which I briefly discuss in an Appendix to this paper, p. 97.

3   It is not my purpose in this paper to explore the historical context of Ruskin's ideas and assumptions. There is certainly room for a paper on that subject, but my purpose here is

though maybe some of the terms we have been regarding as mutually exclusive are not so. For instance, to perceive universals behind particulars need not entail devaluation of the particulars, and it can be argued against the received idea that Christianity is a somewhat materialistic religion. Compare the abstractions that decorate a mosque, for example, with the standard iconography of a Christian church: the animals, the images of labour, the meals, the deep preoccupation with birth and death in their physical reality. The central doctrine of Christianity, the Incarnation, teaches that the Deity put on mortal flesh, and it celebrates that belief in the Eucharist, when bread and wine are transformed into, or received as, flesh and blood.

It is true that the young Ruskin, as an Evangelical, had difficulty with some of this. He could not ignore the significance of the second Commandment:

> Thou shalt not make unto thee any graven image, or any likeness of any thing that is in heaven above, or that is in the earth beneath, or that is in the water under the earth:
> Thou shalt not bow down thyself to them, nor serve them.[4]

It is clear from much of *The Stones of Venice*, especially those passages which try to claim medieval Venice for Protestantism, that Ruskin struggled with the sin of idolatry – feared that he adored graven images too much, or might be charged with doing so. Idolatry is in part the vice of raising matter above spirit.

Yet it is also in Evangelical mode that he insists on the physicality of the Bible's language. In *Modern Painters* IV, how he relishes such splendid images of the psalmist's as 'his hands prepared the dry land',[5] which seems to represent God as a mighty sculptor. The emphasis is pietistic and literalist, but in Ruskin's prose it never seems naive. In much the same way, he admires the surface worldliness of the parables and their concern with everyday economics – labouring in vineyards, sowing seed, earning and investing money. *Unto this Last* might be construed as a book-length meditation on the Parable of the

---

simply to trace a line of thought that runs through Ruskin's work, as I understand it. I should perhaps point out, however, that Ruskin's mistrust of idealism and his emphasis on material things, as well as his belief in the value of active engagement with the physical world, are closely related to the spirit of the age. Like several of his contemporaries – Carlyle above all, but also Browning and Tennyson – Ruskin was schooled in Romanticism but came to mistrust the internalising idealism of Romantic poetry. This notably emerges in his (perhaps surprising) suspicion of Coleridge. In Ruskin's case, the mistrust combined with scorn for the attitudes of the pre-Romantic era: for the eighteenth-century aspiration to 'improve' nature, which I discuss further below. Ruskin, by contrast, celebrates an autonomous universe that is independent of human will and desire.

4   Exodus 20.4–5.

5   Psalm 95.5. Ruskin quotes the Coverdale translation from the Book of Common Prayer.

Vineyard, and then in the book that anticipates *Unto this Last*, *A Joy for Ever*, there is his dazzling homily on the Parable of the Talents. All men are, he says, 'stewards or ministers of whatever talents are entrusted to them'. And he continues thus:

> Only, is it not a strange thing, that while we more or less accept the meaning of that saying, so long as it is considered metaphorical, we never accept its meaning in its own terms? You know the lesson is given us under the form of a story about money. Money was given to the servants to make use of: the unprofitable servant dug in the earth, and hid his Lord's money. Well, we in our poetical and spiritual application of this, say, that of course money doesn't mean money, it means wit, it means intellect, it means influence in high quarters, it means everything in the world except itself. And do you not see what a pretty and pleasant come-off there is for most of us in this spiritual application? Of course, if we had wit, we would use it for the good of our fellow-creatures. But we haven't wit. Of course, if we had influence with the bishops, we would use it for the good of the Church; but we haven't any influence with the bishops. Of course, if we had political power, we would use it for the good of the nation; but we have no political power; we have no talents entrusted to *us* of any sort or kind. It is true we have a little money, but the parable can't possibly mean anything so vulgar as money; our money's our own.
>
> I believe, if you think seriously of this matter, you will feel that the first and most literal application is just as necessary a one as any other – that the story does very specially mean what it says – plain money. (16.98–99)

There is in the irony of this a deep contempt for 'poetical and spiritual' applications: not for the poetical and spiritual as such, but for the cover those categories provide in the thinking of those who wish to avoid *material* implications. To quote a well-known materialist – specifically a dialectical materialist – 'Grub first, then morality'.[6] The Ruskin who wrote *A Joy For Ever* was no longer a rigid Evangelical, yet there is something in the habit of mind my quotation exemplifies which inescapably derives from a more or less fundamentalist up-bringing. At any rate, it belongs to the tradition of scriptural Protestantism with its emphasis on literal interpretations of the word of God. Such literalism, often conservative in effect, is in Ruskin's case subversive.

It is unusual for literalism to be applied to the social teachings of the Bible. It is much more commonly applied to narrative texts – to those parts of scripture that most of us now think of as mythical. We find Ruskin doing this in *Modern Painters* IV, particularly in the chapters on 'The Firmament' and 'The Dry Land', where he has to juggle with a combination of fundamentalism (praising the understanding of the simple Christian), Paleyan Natural Theology, and

6 Bertolt Brecht, *The Threepenny Opera*, II.3.

the latest in Creationist geology: 'What space of time was in reality occupied by the "day" of Genesis, is not, at present, of any importance for us to consider' (6.16) he says, dismissing a question that must have troubled him much more than he would like us to suppose. In 'The Firmament', in fact, he goes some way towards advocating the simple interpretation of scripture, not because it is what he himself believes – it is not clear whether he does or not – but because it seems to bring the reality of God much closer to material experience. He is discussing some quotations from the Psalms, which include the words, 'He bowed the heavens also, and came down; he made darkness pavilions round about him, dark waters, and thick clouds of the skies',[7] and he comments as follows:

> By accepting the words in their simple sense, we are thus led to apprehend the immediate presence of the Deity, and His purpose of manifesting Himself as near us whenever the storm-cloud stoops upon its course; while by our vague and inaccurate acceptance of the words we remove the idea of His presence far from us, into a region which we can neither see nor know; and gradually, from the close realisation of a living God who "maketh the clouds his chariot" we refine and explain ourselves into dim and distant suspicion of an inactive God, inhabiting inconceivable places, and fading into the multitudinous formalisms of the laws of Nature. (6.110)

The target here is plainly Deism and the way rationalistic proofs of divine order lead ultimately to atheism. Thus emphasis on the material, on the physical application of God's word, gives substance to a faith that might otherwise falter. When it comes to the moral teaching of the parables, this is still more urgently the case, and the Ruskin of *A Joy For Ever*, *Unto This Last* and after is preternaturally alert to the slippery evasions whereby well-heeled Protestants can cite scripture to excuse themselves from plain responsibilities. 'Plain money' indeed. There is a remarkable passage in the 1883 Preface to the re-arranged edition of *Modern Painters* II, where Ruskin sums up the theme of his book with the text, 'Happy are the pure in heart, for they shall see God'. His preference for 'Happy' over the 'Blessed' of the Authorised Version,[8] like his preference for 'justice' over 'righteousness' and 'helpful' over 'holy' in *Unto This Last* (17.59–60), constitutes further resistance to the 'poetical and spiritual'. All three substitutions oblige us to consider material arguments. He understands the words in question

> as having reference, like the other Beatitudes, to actual human life, according to the word of Job – "I have heard of thee by the hearing of the ear, but now mine eye

7 Ruskin here conflates and perhaps misremembers Psalm 18.9, 11.
8 Matthew 5.8.

seeth thee;" this revelation being given to Job entirely through the forms and life of the natural world, severally shown him by their unseen Creator. The same confession of faith, after the same instruction, is again uttered by Linnaeus in the beginning of the "Systema ... Naturae:" ... "As one awaked out of sleep, I saw the Lord passing by – eternal, infinite, omniscient, omnipotent, and I stood as in a trance."

The passage is characteristic in at least two ways. There is, first of all, the insistence that to see nature as it should be seen is, in effect, to see God. It is this that gives secular figures like Linnaeus or, pre-eminently, Turner prophetic status on a par with Job's. (I shall pursue this point further when I come to the chapter on Turner's topography in *Modern Painters* IV.) Secondly, this emphasis on the spiritual essence of material things leads ineluctably to moral and social questions, just as it was doing in the course of Ruskin's career. It here becomes the occasion for another assault on self-righteous evasiveness: 'the self-abhorrence of Job, and the awe of Linnaeus, are ... entirely distinct from the spurious and prurient self-condemnation which is the watch-word of modern Protestantism'. The phrase 'pure in heart' should not be mystified into 'the "washing of sanctification"', but should be seen only as 'definite human virtue possible to human effort, and *commanded* in the plain words, "Cleanse your hands, ye sinners; and *purify your hearts, ye double-minded*"' (4.4–5, Ruskin's italics).

Plain words, plain money. But do these examples amount to a form of materialism? Well, no, they don't. But they don't amount to idealism either: not if we take idealism to imply – as perhaps we should not – that the essential reality of things is immaterial and elsewhere. Fundamental to Ruskin's teaching about art, from the very outset, is his conviction that the neo-Classical notion of *improving* nature is impious and arrogant, as the spirit of nature dwells in its particulars. Difference is not imperfection but multitudinousness, variety, redundance, indeed wealth. Each particular thing, for Ruskin, must be understood as a unique manifestation of the common spirit of nature – which is in effect, of course, the love of God. Neo-Classical art, by contrast, seeks to depict the perfect form of any given particular – a form which, by Ruskin's definition, cannot exist, since it is in the nature of nature to be various. Such idealities are in the end deformities; they impose a conventionalised model determined by human limitations on a world which is illimitable and infinite. Thus it is only in the thing itself that nature is made manifest.

The neo-Classical model is largely derived from Aristotelian philosophy. It depends on the doctrine of essential form and takes it that the artist's job is to abstract that form from the imperfect particular. Ruskin, at least in his early books, was hostile to this notion, and on the whole indifferent to Aristotle.[9]

This may appear surprising: one might have expected Aristotle to appeal more than Plato to a thinker who emphasises the material and particular. For if Aristotle leads to idealisation in practice, what might we expect of Plato, for whom the shapes of our experience are merely shadows cast by forms in another realm?

There is, however, at least one major section of Ruskin's work that is directly indebted to Aristotle, and it is this passage more than any other that will help us to identify the balance, in Ruskin's thinking, of the material and the ideal. In the opening chapters of *Modern Painters* II Ruskin repudiates mere *aesthesis* in favour of what he calls, following Aristotle, *theoria*:

> Now the term "aesthesis" properly signifies mere sensual perception of the outward qualities and necessary effects of bodies; in which sense only, if we would arrive at any accurate conclusions on this difficult subject, it should always be used. (4.42)

We should perhaps note the word 'sensual' again here. As with 'sensualism', there is arguably a hint of the lascivious and appetitive, but the meaning is in substance close to 'materialistic' in the popular modern sense. 'But', Ruskin goes on,

> ... I wholly deny that the impressions of beauty are in any way sensual; they are neither sensual nor intellectual, but moral: and for the faculty receiving them, whose difference from mere perception I shall immediately endeavour to explain, no term can be more accurate or convenient than that employed by the Greeks, "Theoretic," which I pray permission, therefore, always to use, and to call the operation of the faculty itself, Theoria. (4.42)

A little further on he adds these definitions:

> The mere animal consciousness of the pleasantness I call Aesthesis; but the exulting, reverent, and grateful perception of it I call Theoria. For this, and this only, is the full comprehension and contemplation of the Beautiful as a gift of God. (4.47)

'Contemplation', in fact, is the word normally used to translate *theoria*, and it links the concept with spiritual discipline. For what Ruskin is saying is that the appreciation of true beauty, whether in art or nature, whether in his terms 'vital' or 'typical', is more than a simple pleasure of the flesh, and something which calls on the whole of our moral being. We should not be misled here into the

9 For Ruskin's attitude to Aristotle, see Dinah Birch, *Ruskin's Myths* (Oxford: Clarendon, 1988), 24–27. Birch points out that Ruskin's dislike of Aristotle was closely related to his dissatisfaction with Oxford philosophy in particular and classical education in general. At the same time, as she shows, Ruskin's early books are indebted to Aristotle for their methods of organisation, and the occasional references to Aristotle in *Modern Painters* were sometimes made, as Ruskin later admitted, 'to show that I had read him' (quoted Birch, p. 14n).

perennial error of therefore converting images into ideas. We are not talking of ideas as such, though ideas are not excluded. We are talking of 'those material sources which are agreeable to our moral nature in its purity and perfection' (4.48).[10]

Can those who do not share Ruskin's faith follow him on this point? Peter Fuller, in his books *Images of God* (1985) and *Theoria: Art, and the Absence of Grace* (1988), argues that they can. He relates *theoria* to the broader doctrine of Truth to Nature. Our sense of beauty, he argues, is derived from nature and our perceptions of it; beauty answers to a biological need. I don't know whether he is right; my instincts certainly tell me that he is. At any rate, it is in this recognition by our human nature of the supreme order and harmony of external nature that we find the Ruskinian balance of the material and the spiritual. This is what Ruskin claims in *Præterita* to have learnt from an aspen-tree near Fontainebleau:

> Languidly, but not idly, I began to draw it; and as I drew, the languor passed away: the beautiful lines insisted on being traced, – without weariness. More and more beautiful they became, as each rose out of the rest, and took its place in the air. With wonder increasing every instant, I saw that they "composed" themselves, by finer laws than any known of men. At last, the tree was there, and everything that I had thought before about trees, nowhere. (35.134)

The inverted commas around 'composed' are significant. To compose things is normally thought of as the artist's job, but these things (Ruskin tells us) '"composed" themselves'. That is one way of saying they were composed by God, the greatest of all artists.

> The woods, which I had looked on as a wilderness, fulfilled I then saw, in their beauty, the same laws which guided the clouds, divided the light, and balanced the wave. "He hath made everything beautiful in his time," became for me thenceforward the interpretation of the bond between the human mind and all visible things. (35.135)

Of course Ruskin is not a materialist! But look at the way in which he is not. He does not reduce particulars to generalities, he does not convert matter into ideas, he does not value physical things for their potential as symbols. Particular beauty, loved for its own sake, becomes the emblem of universal beauty. As Gerard Manley Hopkins wrote of a bluebell: 'I know the beauty of our Lord by it.'[11] When I first read Ruskin, I was puzzled by the fact that this writer who laid so much stress on particulars was indifferent to many painters who seemed to me

10 Ruskin is here quoting himself: *Modern Painters* I (3.110).

11 *The Journals and Papers of Gerard Manley Hopkins*, ed. Humphry House and Graham Storey (London: Oxford University Press, 1959), p. 199.

to excel at rendering them – Constable, for instance, or certain of the Dutch landscapists. I now realise that these painters were, in Ruskin's view, the materialists. Rightly or wrongly, he saw them as lacking the overarching vision of nature that he finds in Turner: in Platonic terms, their particulars do not manifest universals. In the chapter 'Of Turnerian Topography' in *Modern Painters* IV, Ruskin argues this case through Turner's *Pass of Faido*, comparing his own literal representation of the scene with Turner's more visionary account of it. It is in this chapter that Ruskin considers how far the artist 'should permit himself to alter, or, in the usual art language, improve, nature' (6.27). ('Improve' is the usual neo-Classical term.) What is the role, he appears to be asking, of the artist's imagination?

> It is always wrong to draw what you don't see. This law is inviolable. But then, some people see only things that exist, and others see things that do not exist, or do not exist apparently. And if they really *see* these non-apparent things, they are quite right to draw them; the only harm is when people try to draw non-apparent things, who *don't* see them, but think they can calculate or compose into existence what is to them for evermore invisible. (6.27–28, Ruskin's italics)

What Turner sees in the Pass of Faido is partly what he remembers– what he brings to the scene from the day's travelling perhaps and the state of mind it has produced, but more than that. He also brings his knowledge of the Alps, a lifetime's knowledge of mountain landscape, of landscape generally and of 'great creating Nature' herself. Turner's pictures are symbolic or emblematic, in that a single view may embody or imply the whole of life.

The detail speaks of the whole. The universal resides in the particular. Just as a single bar of music may epitomise a symphony, so the aspen-tree from *Præterita* delivers the message that 'He hath made everything beautiful'. It is able to speak of the whole because the whole is a book laid open for us to read: 'the eternal volume' Ruskin calls it elsewhere in volume IV (6.90). It is here that he approaches neo-Platonism. For him, in a way that recalls the seventeenth century, there are two books that reveal God to man. Ruskin would have wholly endorsed these words from Sir Thomas Browne's *Religio Medici* (1642):

> Thus there are two Bookes from whence I collect my Divinity; besides that written one of God, another of his servant Nature, that universall and publik Manuscript, that lies expans'd unto the eyes of all; those that never saw him in the one, have discovered him in the other.[12]

The Ruskin of *Modern Painters* is sometimes almost comic in his confidence that God's unambiguous purpose is there for him to read and expound. He is constantly telling us what God intended us to see and enjoy, what he meant us to understand, what uses he had in mind for this or that.

If nature is a book, it follows that it must contain a language. As Ruskin often reminds us, there are many kinds of language other than speech. Painting and sculpture and architecture are languages as well; to appreciate them properly we have to learn how to read them, just as we do with literature. That this is the case is sometimes obvious. Most people would recognise that Turner's *Slave Ship*[13] has a 'message' for us. Authorities on medieval art agree that the great French cathedrals are complex 'documents' that convey elaborate scholastic arguments. Yet the *Slave Ship*, in Ruskin's famous description, is also in some sense a window on the world. The framing of the scene and the integration of its symbols focus and intensify the meaning of the event which it depicts. One might compare Shakespeare's conceit of the play as something which holds 'the mirror up to nature'.[14] For meaning to be present in picture or play, there must also in some sense be meaning in nature, and sure enough, Ruskin asserts that God's judgement on the slavers is 'written upon the sky in lines of blood' (3.572). The writing is partly the calligraphy of paint, partly an inscription by the hand of God as revealed, in effect, to the prophet Turner.[15] The distinction between art and nature is not absolute for Ruskin. It is a distinction between two creators of vastly differing power. Nature, quite as much as art, was created to please and instruct. When we create works of art, we imitate and emulate the Creator:

> All great art is the expression of man's delight in God's work, not in *his own*. But observe, he is not himself his own work: he is himself precisely the most wonderful piece of God's workmanship extant. (7.263, Ruskin's italics)

In *Modern Painters* IV, when Ruskin meditates in a sequence of chapters on the 'materials' of which the earth is made, he even goes so far as to suggest, not

---

12 *The Works of Sir Thomas Browne*, ed. Geoffrey Keynes, 2nd edn rev., 4 vols (Chicago: University of Chicago Press, 1964), I, 24–25. For a biblical source of this image, see Romans 1.19–20:

> That which may be known of God is manifest in them [i.e. in man]; for God hath shewed it unto them.
>
> For the invisible things of him from the creation of the world are clearly seen, being understood by the things that are made, even his eternal power and Godhead …

Alluding to this passage in *The Stones of Venice* III, Ruskin remarks 'that the whole world, and all that is therein, be it low or high, great or small, is a continual Gospel' (11.184).

13 Ruskin's title for the painting, which he owned. The full and correct title is *Slavers throwing overboard the dead and the dying*.

14 *Hamlet*, III.2.22. 'Nature' in this context means human nature.

15 Ruskin no doubt means to recall the hand-writing on the wall at Belshazzar's feast (Daniel 5.5).

just that mountains are works of divine sculpture, but that God has prepared sculptural materials for humans to cut and carve. 'The earth was without form and void', says the book of Genesis. Then the waters were gathered in one place and the dry land appeared. 'The command that the waters should be *gathered*', says Ruskin, 'was the command that the earth should be *sculptured*' (6.116, Ruskin's italics). A few pages on, when he has embarked on his account of the materials of mountains, he gives these three reasons for the 'appointed frailness of mountains':

> The first, and the most important, that successive soils might be supplied to the plains ... and that men might be furnished with a material for their works of architecture and sculpture, at once soft enough to be subdued, and hard enough to be preserved; the second, that some sense of danger might always be connected with the most precipitous forms, and thus increase their sublimity; and the third, that a subject of perpetual interest might be opened to the human mind in observing the changes of form brought about by time on these monuments of creation. (6.134–35)

It is an amazingly heterogeneous set of reasons. God here has in mind not only the essential economy of the natural order, but the human need to create and appreciate beauty. A few pages further on still, we find Ruskin reflecting on the kinds of sculpture that are achievable in specific kinds of stone. For example:

> The sculptor of granite is forced to confine himself to, and to seek for, certain types of form capable of expression in his material; he is naturally driven to make his figures simple in surface, and colossal in size, that they may bear his blows; and this simplicity and magnitude are exactly the characters necessary to show the granitic or porphyritic colour to the best advantage. And thus we are guided, almost forced, by the laws of nature, to do right in art. (6.143)

There is here in embryo a Ruskinian doctrine that he never finally formulated in words, though it was to become increasingly more central to his thought. Modernist critics have called it 'truth to material', but Ruskin had already given expression to the concept in, for instance, *The Stones of Venice* II (1853):

> To the Gothic workman the living foliage became an object of intense affection, and he struggled to render all its characters with as much accuracy as was compatible with the laws of design and *the nature of his material*. (10.236, my italics)

The latter was quite as important for Ruskin as the former. Good sculpture expressed both the subject depicted and the material in which it was executed. Both the leaf and the stone, after all, are products of nature.

This doctrine of truth to material may help to provide the answer we have been seeking. Ruskin was not a materialist in either the vulgar or the philosophical sense. But he was unable or unwilling to distinguish between a truth and the material that embodied it. It is surely significant that he called his great study of Venetian architecture *The* Stones *of Venice* – not the buildings of it, nor the art. It was Carlyle who noticed that Ruskin had written, as Shakespeare's Duke Senior had read, a '*Sermon* in Stones' (9.xlvi, Carlyle's italics), and Ruskin himself plainly thought of his stones as touchstones, as moral indicators. That they were so, though, did not detract from the weightiness of their substance. First of all, they were plain *stones* as if waiting to be turned into buildings already latent in their nature. Moreover, is there not some sense throughout Ruskin's work that the material world is sufficient in itself? That it is divine, undoubtedly, but *so* divine that he has no need for further divinity? That he prefers the fiery clouds and enflamed peaks to the angels and the heaven with which he compares them in *Præterita* I?

> For me, the Alps and their people were alike beautiful in their snow, and their humanity; and I wanted, neither for them nor myself, sight of any thrones in heaven but the rocks, or of any spirits in heaven but the clouds. (35.115–16)

On the one hand, this is a confession that the boy Ruskin was less religious than he thinks (or perhaps thought) he ought to have been: in a sense, that he was too materialistic. On the other hand, it is a recognition that the supernatural enacts its will in nature and that the theatre where we display the image of God is composed of material things.

APPENDIX

The case made for Ruskin's materialism in Catherine Williams's Ruskin's Philosophy

Catherine Williams's essay summarises the findings of her thesis on the objects collected by Ruskin for the St George's Museum (now the Ruskin Gallery) in Sheffield. The educational theory on which the museum is based, she argues, is unequivocally materialist; and she rightly asserts that 'All Ruskin's work … takes for granted that external reality exists independently of mind and that it can be learned from directly' (p. 2). In support of this contention, she quotes Lenin's definition of materialism, which undoubtedly brings us closer to Ruskin than do the OED definitions cited above:

> The subjectivist line on the question of causality is philosophical idealism … The recognition of objective law in nature and the recognition that this law is reflected with approximate fidelity in the mind of man is materialism. (Quoted p. 2)

And she concludes: 'Ruskin was a materialist … in other words he considered that things produce and confirm ideas, and not ideas, things' (p. 22).

This exactly conforms to my own view, as far as it goes. But it evades the apparent contradiction of Ruskin's adherence to Plato. Williams comments on this as follows:

> Platonic idealism, which detaches the ideal from the object, making it mystical and necessarily superior, is compressed [in Ruskin] into what could be called 'material idealism', in which the ideal only has existence in the real. (p. 11)

As Williams's quotation from Lenin should demonstrate, however, 'material idealism' is oxymoronic. Her account of Ruskin's placing of the ideal is convincing, but she seems to forget that it presupposes, quite as much as pure Platonism does, a teleological universe. As Williams reads Ruskin, a material thing approaches the ideal to the extent that it fulfils its natural function. But for Ruskin the fulfilment of that function is willed by the Creator of the thing, for whom, moreover, it has a destiny.

6

'Job's Iron Pen'

Ruskin's use of engraved illustration in
Modern Painters

ALAN DAVIS

SHORTLY AFTER the six-volume 'Complete Edition' of *Modern Painters* was issued in 1888, prospective purchasers were reminded, in an article by E. T. Cook, that the work was 'a portfolio of engravings, as well as a library of literature'; further, that it was 'in its original form, one of the most elaborate and beautiful collections of illustrations ever issued'.[1] This is indeed so, and yet this aspect of *Modern Painters* has received little attention from twentieth-century scholarship. Among the many possible reasons for this neglect, two are particularly worthy of note. First, the outstanding quality of the *Modern Painters* illustrations is scarcely evident from a perusal of the inadequate reproductions issued with the small (post-1890) editions in which the work is usually read. Even the Cook and Wedderburn Library Edition of Ruskin's *Works* is deficient in this regard, being illustrated chiefly by photogravures of the original plates (reduced in scale), in which much of their delicacy – so important to Ruskin – has been lost. It is important to stress that Ruskin's purposes in his illustrations can be fully understood only through the early editions of the work, which contain original impressions from the steel plates.

The second important reason for neglect is that, for much of the twentieth century, Victorian reproductive steel engraving has been perceived as artistically uninteresting. Although a number of studies of Victorian steel engraving have been published since the 1970s, these have concentrated chiefly on the social

---

1 'Mr. Ruskin and the Booksellers', in E. T. Cook, *Studies in Ruskin* (Orpington and London: Allen, 1890), p. 196. I am grateful to members of the Ruskin Seminar at Lancaster University for many helpful discussions during the preparation of this paper.

and cultural context.[2] A significant re-evaluation of the specifically artistic merits of Victorian engraving in general seems unlikely. Nevertheless, it is important to attempt an analysis of Ruskin's work in this area for several reasons: first, because many of the *Modern Painters* illustrations represent a sustained attempt to extend the capabilities of engraving as an interpretative medium; secondly, because such an analysis is necessary to a full understanding of *Modern Painters*; and thirdly, because of the insight which such a study offers into Ruskin himself. For Ruskin, who considered that 'a square inch of man's engraving is worth all the photographs that ever were dipped in acid' (19.89), engraving was of far greater significance than its use as a mere method of reproducing pictures would imply, and its importance for him never diminished. Even after preparing a series of Oxford lectures devoted entirely to engraving, he was still driven to express regret at 'the imperfection of all I have been able to say' about the subject (28.460–61).

This paper attempts to restore something of Ruskin's sense of the importance of engraving to a reading of *Modern Painters*, but its scope is limited to a study of line engraving. Nothing is said here of Ruskin's keen sense of propriety with regard to the use of particular types of print-making – a sense which had significant implications for the development of the *Modern Painters* illustrations between 1856 and 1860, and which leads inevitably to a discussion of Ruskin's work as an etcher in the volumes published during that period. These are important matters, and will be treated in a subsequent paper. The aim of the present paper is to examine Ruskin's concept of line engraving as an art form, to explore the way in which his concept of 'finish' influenced his collaborative work with the engravers during the production of the engraved plates for *Modern Painters*, and to compare Ruskin's approach to engraving with that of Turner. We begin, however, with a brief discussion of the development of steel engraving in Britain, insofar as it relates directly to Ruskin's work for *Modern Painters*.

In 1822 Thomas Lupton, one of the engravers who collaborated with Turner for the *Liber Studiorum*, successfully engraved a mezzotint portrait on a steel plate which yielded more than a thousand impressions.[3] The use of steel was a

2 See for example: Hilary Beck, *Victorian Engravings* (London: Victoria and Albert Museum, 1973); Basil Hunnisett, *A Dictionary of British Steel Engravers* (London: Lewis, 1980); Basil Hunnisett, *Steel-engraved Book Illustration in England* (London: Scolar, 1980); Hilary Guise, *Great Victorian Engravings* (London: Astragal, 1980); Anthony Dyson, *Pictures to Print: The nineteenth-century engraving trade* (London: Farrand, 1984); Basil Hunnisett, *An Illustrated Dictionary of British Steel Engravers* (Aldershot: Scolar, 1989).

highly significant development. Previously, copper plates had been used for both etching and engraving, but the limited durability of copper had important commercial implications. A typical line engraving on copper could yield only a few hundred impressions of good quality, and a mezzotint plate yielded even fewer. For example, no more than two hundred impressions were taken from each plate for Turner's *Liber Studiorum*, but it was necessary to carry out substantial reworking of the mezzotint several times during printing because the condition of the plate steadily deteriorated. The introduction of steel plates during the 1820s meant that a line engraving could be made to yield many thousands of impressions of high quality, but it also brought about a change in the actual style of engraving. The hardness of the metal led quite naturally to the use of finer lines, and hence to a beguiling delicacy which, though superficially attractive, is usually blamed for an overall decline in the art. The reason for the decline was identified as early as 1841 by T. H. Fielding, who in his book *The Art of Engraving* attacked what he called the 'excessively finished style of the present day' – a style which, he maintained, 'tends to reduce all engravers to the same level, or what is still worse, allows some whose only merit consists in a capability of laying lines closer than others, to usurp the place of real talent'.[4]

Still, the popularity of the so-called 'highly finished' quality of steel engravings, together with the favourable economics of printing large numbers of impressions, led to a rapid growth in the publication of illustrated books and, notably, the illustrated annuals such as *Friendship's Offering* (to which the young Ruskin contributed poems) and *The Keepsake* during the 1820s and 1830s. By the 1840s, the fashion for the annuals was fading, but steel engraving continued for many years to be the most prestigious method for reproducing pictures until it was eventually superseded by the perfection of photomechanical processes. The transition was gradual, but we might sensibly mark the end of the era as 1890 – the year in which *The Art Journal* published its final steel engraving.[5]

From this background of painstaking but uninspired reproductive craftsmanship, it was still possible for work of great character to emerge, but it required close collaboration and deep mutual understanding between artist and engraver. By far the most successful partnership of the period, and the one

---

3　Percy Muir, *Victorian Illustrated Books* (1971; rev. London: Batsford, 1985), p. 67. Further information concerning Lupton's involvement with Turner and the *Liber Studiorum* may be found in Gillian Forrester, *Turner's 'Drawing Book': The Liber Studiorum* (London: Tate Gallery, 1996).

4　Dyson, p. 132.

5　This last plate was, one might think appropriately, engraved by J. C. Armytage. See Hunnisett, *Illustrated Dictionary*, p. 12.

which is of the greatest importance in the context of the present study, was that which existed between Turner and his engravers. Turner regarded the engraving process not merely as a means of reproducing existing pictures, but rather as the means of creating new works of art in a monochrome medium which, happily, enabled them to be multiplied. Having already had considerable experience of working with engravers on copper, he soon came to appreciate the potential of steel for conveying atmospheric effects. Working in close collaboration with his engravers, and painstakingly correcting their work at each stage of production, he succeeded in creating prints such as those for Rogers's *Italy* (1830) and *Poems* (1834) which have been generally acknowledged as the finest examples of their kind. Having supervised the engraving process, Turner considered the prints to be, in a sense, his own work, and he was willing for them to be judged as such. Seen in this light, Ruskin's frequent reference to Turner engravings in *Modern Painters* is justifiable. It made good sense on other grounds, too: even as late as 1908, Turner was described as being 'largely known to the world through his engravings'.[6]

By the time Ruskin began to illustrate *Modern Painters*, beginning with the third volume published in 1856, Turner was dead, and the school of landscape engraving he had so patiently developed was in decline. But by then Ruskin's own experience of the many aspects of the engraving process was considerable. Examples of his work had been engraved for the annuals as early as 1843, bringing him into contact with engravers such as J. C. Armytage who had worked with Turner.[7] He had prepared his own soft-ground etchings for the first edition of *The Seven Lamps of Architecture* in 1849; and for *The Stones of Venice* (1851–53) he had worked closely with some of the finest engravers in England. All this experience was to result, in the final three volumes of *Modern Painters*, in one of the most fascinating collaborative exercises in nineteenth-century print-making.

Before considering the *Modern Painters* engravings themselves, it is important that we should understand what Ruskin actually expected from engraving as an art form. Although he made various comments about engraving during the 1850s in books such as *The Harbours of England* and *The Elements of Drawing* (and of course in *Modern Painters* itself), his sustained writing on the subject came later: first, in a series of articles published in *The Art Journal* under the title *The Cestus*

6   W. G. Rawlinson, *The Engraved Work of J. M. W. Turner, R.A.*, 2 vols (London: Macmillan, 1908–13), I, ix.

7   For Ruskin's illustrations, engraved by Armytage for *Friendship's Offering* 1843–44, see Jan Piggott, *Turner's Vignettes* (London: Tate Gallery, 1993), p. 91.

of Aglaia in 1865–66; and subsequently, in the Oxford lectures of 1872 published as *Ariadne Florentina* (1873–76). Of course there is some risk of being misled if we examine the engravings for *Modern Painters* in the light of opinions expressed by Ruskin ten or fifteen years later, but the approach can be justified on two counts. First, we should note that although Ruskin's ideas about engraving do show development over the years, they are nevertheless consistent; their growth, as Ruskin would say, is 'that of a tree – not of a cloud' (7.9). Secondly, we should observe that his mature opinions of the 1860s and 1870s must have been based largely on his own experience – notably on his most sustained and intense period of print-making during the late 1850s for *Modern Painters*. (He published few, if any, engravings in the 1860s.) The approach here, then – to some extent dictated by the available material – is to study the destination in the hope of shedding light upon the nature of the journey.

Making a startling contrast with the high level of sophistication involved in Victorian print-making, Ruskin insists, early in *Ariadne Florentina*, on the fundamental nature of engraving:

> A line is the simplest work of art you can produce … . The primitive line, the first and last, generally the best of lines, is that which you have elementary faculty of at your fingers' ends … – the scratch. (22.319–20)

This leads him on to contemplate the permanence of engraving – a concept which is central to all his writing on the subject: 'Engraving … is essentially the cutting into a solid substance for the sake of making your ideas as permanent as possible, – graven with an iron pen in the Rock for ever' (22.320). The allusion here is to the book of Job: 'Oh that my words were now written! oh that they were printed in a book! That they were graven with an iron pen and lead in the rock for ever!' (Job 19.23–24). It is likely that Ruskin's use of the 'iron pen' image owes something to Blake, who had made powerful use of it in one of the plates of his series of engravings illustrating the book of Job (PLATE 3) – engravings with which Ruskin had been familiar since the 1840s, and which he greatly admired. But whatever its origin, the same point is emphasized by Ruskin again and again: '*Permanence*, you observe, is the object, not multiplicability; – that is quite an accidental … attribute of engraving' (22.320).

There were, of course, good commercial reasons why a publisher of engravings would wish his plates to be durable, and some engravers acquired high reputations for their ability to produce work which would stand up to the stresses of long print runs. But it was clearly more than mere economics which caused Ruskin, writing a new preface for *Seven Lamps* in 1880, to express delight in

PLATE 3. Plate 11 from William Blake's series of engraved illustrations
of the book of Job (1826).

Armytage's plates which had by then done service in many thousands of impressions for *Modern Painters*. He admired, he said, not only

> their extreme delicacy, but their permanence. Some of his plates ... show scarcely
> any loss of brightness for any use hitherto made of them. (8.16)

After stressing the permanence of engraving, Ruskin goes on in *Ariadne Florentina* to consider the mechanical difficulty involved:

> Engraving ... requires always force, and its virtue is that of a line produced by pressure .... It involves, therefore, always, ideas of power and dexterity, but also of restraint; and the delight you take in it should involve an understanding of the difficulty the workman dealt with .... The main use of the restraint which makes the line difficult to draw, is to give time and motive for deliberation in drawing it, and to ensure its being the best in your power. (22.322–23)

Because of the essential permanence of engraving, and because of the difficulties that must be overcome, Ruskin argues that 'the engraved line is therefore to be conclusive; not experimental. "I have determined this," says the engraver .... This is so, and must for ever be so, he tells you' (22.323). Engraving, therefore, for Ruskin, is the appropriate medium for the noble utterance – the kind of statement described in *Sesame and Lilies* (1865), which the artist would fain set down 'for ever; engrave it on rock if he could; saying, "This is the best of me; for the rest, I ate and drank, and slept, loved, and hated, like another; my life was as the vapour and is not; but this I saw and knew: this, if anything of mine, is worth your memory"' (18.61). It follows that the alternative to thoughtful work in engraving is consummate folly; or, as Ruskin puts it:

> Look, – all the world, – look for evermore, says the foolish engraver; see what a fool I have been. How many lines I have laid for nothing! (22.323)

In *The Cestus of Aglaia*, similar arguments had led Ruskin to consider the moral obligation implicit in the art of engraving. There are consequences to be considered (and again we find the allusion to Job):

> Here is a steel point, and 'tis like Job's "iron pen" – and you are going to cut into steel with it, in a most deliberate way, as into the rock for ever. And this scratch or inscription of yours will be seen of a multitude of eyes .... This multipliable work will pass through thousand thousand hands, strengthen and inform innumerable souls, if it be worthy, vivify the folly of thousands if unworthy .... Remember, also, it will mix in the very closest manner in domestic life .... Where will you look for a chance of saying something nobly, if it is not here? (19.100–1)

By contrast, the moral consequence of making the wrong choices is, he warns, to 'bite permanent mischief in with acid; to spread an inked infection of evil all your days' (19.105).

In *Ariadne Florentina* the symbolism implicit in the act of engraving is further developed. Ruskin begins with the engraver's burin:

PLATE 4. *The Last Furrow*: enlarged facsimile from *Ariadne Florentina*
of the wood engraving after Holbein.

The instrument with which the substance, whether of the wood or steel, is cut away,
is the same. It is a solid ploughshare. (22.348)

The image of the burin as a ploughshare was not new. Ruskin had first used it in
the 1850s, in the third volume of *Modern Painters*, writing disparagingly of
engravers who covered 'their paper with certain lines, which they have been
taught to plough in copper, as a husbandman ploughs in clay' (5.158). This was
a highly uncharacteristic comparison, however. Soon afterwards, Ruskin was to

relate the ploughing image to the act of engraving in a fundamentally different and more profound way.

In 1857, for example, in *The Elements of Drawing*, we find him contemplating the symbolic significance of an abandoned plough in the foreground of a Turner engraving (15.206). A few years later, in *Unto This Last* (1860, 1862), he was to discuss the meaning of the word 'capital' in terms of ploughshares, pointing out that the appropriate question concerned not the number of ploughs possessed, but rather, 'where are your furrows?'. The essence of the matter, he maintained, was the use to which a plough was put:

> What substance will it furnish, good for life? What work construct, protective of life? (17.99)

These are questions which could equally be asked of the engraver's burin. When we recall his reference, in *The Elements of Drawing*, to the labour of the engraver as an example of 'how people must work, in this world, who have really to *do* anything in it' (15.78), we can see how Ruskin, during the later 1850s, was moving steadily towards a symbolic perception of the engraver as ploughman.

The most complete expression of the idea, however, is found in *Ariadne Florentina*, in Ruskin's discussion of a woodcut from Holbein's *Dance of Death* series. Entitled *The Last Furrow*, the subject of the woodcut is a 'ploughman ploughing at evening' (PLATE 4). Here the various strands of Ruskin's concept of engraving are brought together in the many-layered symbolism of a single image – that of the ploughman bent upon his life's work – presented to us, appropriately, through the medium of engraving itself; 'one of the best wood engravings ever produced by art', says Ruskin (22.352), and he continues:

> The husbandman is old and gaunt, and has passed his days … pressing the iron into the ground. And the payment for his life's work is, that he is clothed in rags, and his feet are bare on the clods … . But all the air is full of warmth and of peace; and, beyond his village church, there is, at last, light indeed. His horses lag in the furrow, and his own limbs totter and fail: but one comes to help him. "It is a long field," says Death; "but we'll get to the end of it to-day, – you and I." (22.355)

Thus the fundamental scratch of the engraver depicts the making of the fundamental furrow of the ploughman, and reminds us of the last of all furrows – the grave itself. Ruskin's conception of the symbolic link between the engraving process and the image it produces again suggests comparison with Blake. In Plate 11 of the Job series of engravings, Blake clearly intends the means of producing the plate to be an essential part of the symbolic structure (PLATE 3).

The engraving depicts Job dreaming; within the image, the deity points to tablets of stone on which the Law is recorded – for Blake, the negative aspect of the 'iron pen'. Around the image, in the margin of the plate, Blake has inscribed the actual 'iron pen' text. Finally, by implication, the engraving itself is a creation of the positive aspect of the 'iron pen' – a work of art. This interlocking symbolic structure, in which the image is linked with the means of its production, is so very similar to Ruskin's analysis of the Holbein that one cannot help but suspect this to be the source of Ruskin's concept.

A concept of engraving which approaches this level of complexity does indeed seem to have been forming in Ruskin's mind much earlier, during the writing of *Modern Painters* IV in the mid-1850s. The evidence is found in the chapter entitled 'The Dry Land'. Ruskin begins by quoting from Genesis: 'And God said, Let the waters which are under the heaven be gathered together unto one place, and let the dry land appear' (6.115). The imagery of the passage which then follows is of great significance:

> ... as we read the mighty sentence, "Let the dry land appear," we should try to follow the finger of God, as it engraved upon the stone tables of the earth the letters and the law of its everlasting form; as, gulf by gulf, the channels of the deep were ploughed. (6.116)

Here, then, in speaking of the very creation of the world, Ruskin is employing imagery which takes us to the heart of his concept of engraving: God the engraver cuts the valleys of the earth with the divine burin; God the ploughman ploughs the channels of the deep. Thus is the reader guided, by implication, towards the perception of a parallel symbolism in the creation of the plates of *Modern Painters*, where Ruskin himself, guided by Turner, 'follows the finger of God', and engraves the eternal truths of nature, not on tablets of stone, but on plates of steel.

Finally, we may usefully compare Ruskin's image of the weary, ill-rewarded ploughman with contemporary descriptions of the working conditions of the typical engraver – conditions with which Ruskin was very familiar. The publisher Algernon Graves recorded, for example, that 'engravers earned their money by great manual toil, and very slowly; ... their whole souls were in their work, and many an evening when I have visited them I have found them hard at work with their burin or scraper by gaslight'.[8] Or, in the words of C. W. Radcliffe, one of Turner's engravers: 'few men have more lacked the sympathy and appreciation of the public than engravers; few men have been less known, few have

8   Guise, p. 6.

lived more solitary or more laborious lives'.[9] Of this labour Ruskin became deeply appreciative. 'My friends of the field of steel', he called them, speaking warmly of their 'patience, and deliberate subtlety, and unostentatious will' (19.88). But of course patience, craftsmanship and labour alone were not enough:

> What there is of mechanical in your work; of habitual and thoughtless, of vulgar or servile – for that, indeed, the time has come … I tell you – … a square inch of man's engraving is worth all the photographs that ever were dipped in acid … – only it must be man's engraving, not machine's engraving. You have founded a school on patience and labour – only; that school must soon be extinct. You will have to found one on thought, which is Phoenician in immortality, and fears no fire. (19.89)

John Hayman has suggested that Ruskin's preoccupation with engraving may have been nostalgic in nature – referring back to the steel-engraved annuals of his childhood.[10] Such a view, however, seems to overlook the essentially forward-looking nature of Ruskin's attitude as expressed above; indeed, the engraved work of the annuals represented all that Ruskin most deplored about contemporary engraving practices. Rather than seeking a return to some idealized engraving past, Ruskin looked forward to what he conceived as a progressive school of engraving – one which, indeed, 'fears no fire'. It is in the plates of the last three volumes of *Modern Painters* that we see the outcome of his most important attempt to give direction to such a school.

In the context of *Modern Painters*, the type of 'noble utterance' for which Ruskin considered engraving to be the appropriate and permanent medium of expression is inextricably linked with his concept of 'finish'. This had been introduced in the third edition of the first volume in 1846, when he had warned painters to 'beware of finishing, for the sake of finish', pointing out that any given degree of finish, whether high or low, was acceptable only as the outcome of thought or feeling (3.178). In volume II of the same year he described finish as 'the full and ultimate rendering' of beauty (4.138). By 1853, in the second volume of *The Stones of Venice*, his ideas on finish were developed in more detail. Stating that 'it requires consummate knowledge to finish consummately', he argues that 'the rule is simple':

> Always look for invention first, and after that, for such execution as will help the

9 Rawlinson, I, lxix.

10 John Hayman, *John Ruskin and Switzerland* (Ontario:Wilfrid Laurier University Press, 1990), pp. 9–10.

invention, and as the inventor is capable of without painful effort, and *no more*. Above all, demand no refinement of execution where there is no thought ... and never imagine there is reason to be proud of anything that can be accomplished by patience and sandpaper. (10.199)

This is, broadly, the attitude to finish which Ruskin presented three years later, when devoting a whole chapter to the topic in *Modern Painters* III. True finish, he says, 'does not consist in smoothing or polishing, but in the completeness of the expression of ideas' (5.155). To finish farther 'we must *know* more or *see* more' (5.157); and again 'labour without added knowledge can only blacken or stain a picture, it cannot finish it' (5.164). He summarizes his position at the close of the chapter by concluding that '"finishing" means in art simply "telling more truth"; and that whatever we have in any sort begun wisely, it is good to finish thoroughly' (5.168).

To illustrate his meaning he presents, in his Plate 5, several facsimiles of engraved representations of tree trunks, drawn from a variety of sources. As examples of what Ruskin considered to be the ignoble use of the 'iron pen' they are highly relevant to our present discussion, because all of them, he points out, 'are not finished in any sense but this, – that the paper has been covered with lines' (5.158). In the examples given, the engravers have followed the almost universal practice, whether working on copper or steel, of resorting to conventional patterns of lines which have no particular representational or expressive value; the patterns have been used merely because they form part of the engraver's standard repertoire. P. G. Hamerton, writing in 1876, summed up the situation very clearly:

> The degradation of line-engraving was complete when a tradition had at length regulated every method of interpretation, and, leaving nothing to the instinct and feeling of the workman, prescribed for him where to put thick lines and thin lines, and lozenges with dots in the middle ... . To cut lines regularly and put dots neatly became an aim itself.[11]

It is only through an awareness of the prevalence of this type of work among engravers that we can fully understand Ruskin's praise of his engravers in the Preface to *Modern Painters* III: in executing his plates the engravers had, he said, 'overcome difficulties of a nature often widely differing from those involved by their habitual practice' (5.10). One aspect of that 'habitual practice' is discussed with particular clarity in *The Elements of Drawing* of 1857. Advising the reader to copy various portions of selected engravings, Ruskin continues:

---

11 P. G. Hamerton, *Etching and Etchers* (1876; rpt. Wakefield: EP Publishing, 1975), p. 17.

> Only remember that all engravers' foregrounds are bad; wherever you see the pecu-
> liar wriggling parallel lines of modern engraving become distinct, you must not
> copy; nor admire: it is only the softer masses, and distances, and portions of foliage
> in the plates … which you may copy. (15.78)

The kind of foreground work of which he was complaining is illustrated in
PLATE 5, which is an enlarged detail of one of Turner's plates. Ruskin was still
attacking the use of these 'coarsely broken and wriggled' lines in engravers'
foregrounds fifteen years later in *Ariadne Florentina*. They are, he explains, 'entirely erroneous in principle, for the surface of stones and leaves is not broken
or jagged in this manner, but consists of mossy, or blooming, or otherwise
organic texture, which cannot be represented by these coarse lines' (22.373). It is
important to note here that the engraving conventionalisms which Ruskin most
deplored were apparently fully acceptable to Turner. Although Turner took great
pains to ensure that his engravers fulfilled his requirements, he evidently made
no attempt to eliminate the 'broken and wriggled' lines of which Ruskin com-
plains, as PLATE 5 clearly shows. We should note also that three of Ruskin's
engravers had themselves worked with Turner (Cousen, Armytage and Lupton),
while Le Keux came from a family of engravers with strong Turner connections.

To examine Ruskin's proposed solution to the problem of engraving
foregrounds, and thereby elucidate his ideas about the truly noble employment
of the 'iron pen', it is convenient to turn to a work which he illustrated in the
fifth volume of *Modern Painters* (1860): Turner's *Richmond from the Moors*. The
original watercolour, made for the *England and Wales* series and subsequently
owned by Ruskin, was engraved on copper by J. T. Willmore in 1828 (PLATE 6).[12]
We can be certain that the production of the engraving was supervised by
Turner, since at least one engraver's proof, touched by him, has survived.[13]
(PLATE 5, in fact, is an enlarged detail of the foreground in the left-hand corner
of this plate.) Ruskin invites us to compare the 1828 engraving with his Plate
61, which is an etching made by J. C. Armytage, reduced from a pen drawing
made by Ruskin from Turner's watercolour. (We should note, in passing, the
layering of successive interpretative processes involved here, which is typical of
most of the illustrations of Turner's work in *Modern Painters*.) This etching,
Ruskin tells us, 'will look a little better under a magnifying glass' – and PLATE 7,
therefore, presents the lower left-hand corner of the etching, enlarged as he

12 The watercolour is reproduced in Eric Shanes, *Turner's England* (London: Cassell, 1990), p.
185.
13 Rawlinson, I, 131.

PLATE 5. Enlarged foreground detail from the engraving by J. T. Willmore (1828)
after Turner's *Richmond.*

PLATE 6. Engraving by J. T. Willmore (1828) after Turner's *Richmond.*

suggests. But, Ruskin continues, 'only a most costly engraving of the real size could give any idea of the richness of mossy and ferny leafage included in the real design' (7.128). Nevertheless, the etching clearly demonstrates how Ruskin, through Armytage, has tried to make each line expressive of some particular feature which he has perceived in Turner's watercolour. This is in marked contrast to the earlier print, in which Willmore has used patterns of lines which do little more than establish tone and a crude sense of texture. Despite the reduction in scale (Armytage's etching is somewhat smaller than Willmore's engraving), and despite Willmore's use of copper rather than steel, the comparison, insists Ruskin, will show 'how much yet remains to be done before any approximately just representation of Turner foreground can be put within the reach of the public' (7.128). Driving his point further home, Ruskin does, in fact, go on to present us with such a 'just representation' in his Plate 62 (PLATE 8). Again engraved by Armytage, the plate depicts the lower left-hand corner of Turner's watercolour. If we compare this plate, with its sensitivity to atmosphere and its delicate rendering of leaf and rock forms, with the same portion of the 1828 engraving (PLATE 5), we have a particularly telling illustration of Ruskin's concept of 'finish' as applied to the engraved interpretation of a Turner watercolour.

The quest for a truly Ruskinian 'finish' appears to have inspired his engravers, and Ruskin himself supervised their work no less painstakingly than Turner might have done. Yet Ruskin's preoccupations in this matter were not those of Turner, for whom an engraving was not merely a black-and-white reproduction of an existing watercolour. Turner's notes for his lectures on perspective in 1810 show clearly that he considered the engraving process to be more akin to an act of translation than to an act of copying: 'Engraving is or ought to be a translation of a Picture, for the nature of each art varies ... in the means of expressing the same objects'.[14] For Turner, the original watercolour existed as a starting point for a creative process whose end result was a black-and-white image capable of being multiplied and possessing its own integrity as a work of art. In achieving that end, Turner commonly introduced changes to a design during the proof-correcting stages in order to accommodate the particular demands of the engraving medium for a particular work. Such developmental changes varied widely in both nature and degree, according to the needs of the work in question. For example *Pæstum*, for the 1830 edition of Rogers's *Italy*, was developed so that the sky in the finished engraved vignette is dark and thunderous,

14 Quoted in Anne Lyles and Diane Perkins, *Colour into Line: Turner and the Art of Engraving* (London: Tate Gallery, 1989), p. 11.

PLATE 7. Enlarged foreground detail from the etching by J. C. Armytage
after Turner's *Richmond*, from *Modern Painters* V.

PLATE 8. Engraving by J. C. Armytage illustrating the foreground of Turner's *Richmond*
to a high degree of finish, from *Modern Painters* V.

with bright lightning bolts which were barely hinted at in the original watercolour.[15] While proof-correcting *The Fall of the Rebel Angels*, for the 1835 edition
of Milton's *Poetical Works*, Turner made substantial modifications to the contrast and distribution of light and shade in the design, and requested the engraver, Goodall, to add 'innumerable figures' at the top of the vignette.[16] Often

the changes were less dramatic than this but still significant, involving the addition of dark accents or white highlights in order to correct the overall tonal balance of the final image. Indeed, tales of Turner's fluid attitude to the development of an engraving abound, and J.T. Bunce's comments are as apt as any: 'there were few, if any, of the plates engraved from his works upon which there are not traces of his own hand – a bit of dark, a point of light, a new sweep of line, an alteration of light and shade – worked out in consultation with the engraver, and by him translated from rough hints into intelligible and effective shape'.[17]

This developmental process, so essential to Turner's purposes, was one with which Ruskin had little sympathy; in which regard a passage from *The Harbours of England* (whose text was completed in 1855 – the same year that Ruskin began his intense involvement in engraving work for the third and fourth volumes of *Modern Painters*) is worth quoting at length:

> All his [Turner's] truly fine drawings are either done quickly, or at all events straight forward, without alteration: he never, as far as I have examined his works hitherto, altered but to destroy. When he saw a plate look somewhat dead or heavy, as, compared with the drawing, it was almost sure at first to do, he used to scratch out little lights all over it, and make it "sparkling"; a process in which the engravers almost unanimously delighted, and over the impossibility of which they now mourn, declaring it to be hopeless to engrave after Turner, since he cannot now scratch their plates for them. It is quite true that these small lights were always placed beautifully; and though the plate, after its "touching", generally looked as if ingeniously salted out of her dredging-box by an artistical cook, the salting was done with a spirit which no one else can now imitate. But the original power of the work was for ever destroyed. (13.64–65)

It so happens that in respect of the particular engraving which Ruskin was discussing here – Lupton's mezzotint of Turner's *Portsmouth* – one is inclined to agree that Turner's addition of highlights was excessive. What is more important, however, is that Ruskin objected to the practice in principle. Ruskin's comment, that Turner never 'altered but to destroy' when he made changes to his engraved work in progress, is an extraordinary statement to make about an artist for whom engraving was of central importance in his *oeuvre*. The preparation of engravings after his own work had not been some peripheral activity, but a major occupation of Turner's: during his career he had supervised the creation of many hundreds of different prints, in collaboration with engravers who,

15 Piggott, p. 82, ill. 7, and p. 103, ill. 22.
16 Ibid., pp. 60, 77.
17 Ibid., p. 25, where Bunce's comments are quoted.

through his intensive process of proof-correction, had been effectively trained by Turner specifically for the purpose of engraving his own work. Ruskin's dismissal of Turner's whole approach to the engraving process is therefore quite startling in its audacity. But where Turner saw engraving as an extension of the creative process, Ruskin's motivation, as we have seen above, was primarily symbolic: the essence of the use of the 'iron pen' was its ability to make a permanent record of a once-and-for-all noble utterance. On this basis, an engraved image could be nothing other than a more-or-less accurate copy of an original work.

It is not surprising, therefore, to find that Ruskin's practice in *Modern Painters*, whether supervising engravings from Turner, or from his own drawings, was quite unlike Turner's. Ruskin sought equivalent literal, mark-for-mark expression, in the black-and-white language of engraving, for each nuance that he discerned in the original drawing or watercolour in order to preserve it, unchanged, as far as possible. Ruskin's correspondence with the engraver John Le Keux offers useful insight into Ruskin's ideas concerning the supervision of the engraving process, in which the quest is invariably for accuracy of facsimile, whether of drawing, or (as in one case) of daguerreotype. 'Why have you done the wall ... so [sketch] instead of facsimile my work', he writes; 'Your trees look better than mine through magnifying glass, but are not so good in reality – Try if you can't get them liker mine'; 'you must try to put into the daguerreotype no more than you see ... what I <u>want</u> is the photograph exactly'.[18]

Thus the motivation for Ruskin's engraving is essentially reproductive and interpretative: each original touch of the Master is interpreted and permanently recorded by an appropriate mark, or pattern of marks, in the steel. Throughout the process, the original watercolour or drawing remains the fixed standard, the noble utterance, against which the engraving is judged. This contrasts with Turner's translational and developmental search for an engraved image which, when complete, possesses its own self-consistent unity.

In supervising the engraving of Turner's work for *Modern Painters*, therefore, Ruskin continually exercised a subtle but significant form of editorship. In striving to engrave from Turner's watercolours with the utmost fidelity, he inevitably distorted Turner's own artistic process: the engraved images which Ruskin presents to us are not the images which Turner himself would have produced, even if allowance is made for the fragmentary nature of most of Ruskin's illustrations. In consequence, the illustrations of Turner's work in *Modern Painters* are always

18 *Autograph letters of John Ruskin, with several of his sketches and proofs, chiefly relating to 'Modern Painters'* (London, 1878), Victoria and Albert Museum microfilm (Micro 85).

PLATE 9. Engraving by J. Cousen after Turner's *Goldau*, from *Modern Painters* IV.

immediately recognizable as Ruskinian in style.

The plates of the final three volumes of *Modern Painters* contain the fruits of Ruskin's most highly concentrated attempt to explore and extend the expressive capabilities of English landscape engraving in line. Their subjects are mainly Ruskin's own drawings from nature, or fragments of Turner, rendered with meticulous finish. It is only at the end of volume IV, in the 50th plate, that we are presented, for the first time, with a fully-worked line engraving of a complete, 'finished' Turner watercolour (PLATE 9). (It is also the last time: Ruskin made no comparable attempt to reproduce a major Turner work in its entirety, by line engraving, in volume V.) The plate in question is a representation of Turner's *Goldau* – one of the great Swiss watercolours of 1843 and, for Ruskin, one of the 'truest and mightiest' of his works (13.485). In the Preface to volume IV, Ruskin expressed some disappointment in the engraving: it 'omits, owing to its reduction', he said, 'half the refinements of the foreground' (6.4). Yet it clearly represents the climax of the series of illustrations in volumes III and IV. As we should expect, it shows no trace of the infamous 'broken and wriggled' lines in its foreground. Here is one of Turner's finest pictures, engraved by one of Turner's finest engravers – John Cousen – working once more under close supervision; not by Turner, now, but by Ruskin. Here, approaching full visual expression in the book for the first and last time, is Ruskin's vision of Turner: engraved with an iron pen in the rock for ever.

APPENDIX

RUSKIN BIBLIOGRAPHY
1986–1995

THIS BIBLIOGRAPHY was compiled by David Barron and includes edited works by Ruskin and works on Ruskin published over the last ten years. It is based partly upon a list kindly provided by James S. Dearden which continues from 'Recent Books and Articles' in *The Ruskin Newsletter*, 34/35 (Spring 1989), and aims to continue in the tradition of that most helpful bibliographical listing. It is also based upon the Ruskin Programme's own bibliography, compiled by Michael Wheeler and Lyn Hitch. Barron then added further entries from other bibliographical sources.

In future *Time & Tide* will contain an *annotated* bibliography for the previous year. Proposed entries for 1996 (to be published in 1997) should be sent to **Mr David Barron and Dr Francis O'Gorman**, future joint editors of the Bibliography, c/o **The Ruskin Programme, Bowland College, Lancaster University, LA1 4YT**. Any gifts of new books or offprints from authors or publishers will be gratefully received and passed to the Curator of the Ruskin Library at Lancaster University, Mr Stephen Wildman.

WORKS BY RUSKIN

Ruskin, John, 'Venezia: salvaguardare, conservare, collezionare', *Domus*, no. 671 (April 1986), 12–13 [reproduces specimens of Ruskin's daguerreotypes of Italian architecture].

Ruskin, John, *The Art Criticism of John Ruskin*, ed. by Robert L. Herbert (New York: Da Capo, 1987).

Ruskin, John, *The Correspondence of John Ruskin and Charles Eliot Norton*, ed. by John Lewis Bradley and Ian Ousby (Cambridge: Cambridge University Press, 1987).

Ruskin, John, *The Literary Criticism of John Ruskin*, ed. by Harold Bloom (New York: Da Capo, 1987).

Ruskin, John, *Modern Painters,* ed. by David Barrie, abridged edn (London: Deutsch; New York: Knopf, 1987).

Ruskin, John, *Præterita: The Autobiography of John Ruskin*, introd. by Kenneth Clark (Oxford: Oxford University Press, 1989).

Ruskin, John, *Christmas Story: John Ruskin's Venetian Letters of 1876–77 ... with an Introductory Essay on Ruskin and the Spiritualists, his Quest for the Unseen*, ed. by Van Akin Burd (Newark, NJ: University of Delaware Press; London: Associated University Press, 1990).

Ruskin, John, *Ruskin on Turner*, ed. by Dinah Birch (Boston: Little; London: Cassell, 1990).

Ruskin, John, *A Tour to the Lakes in Cumberland: John Ruskin's Diary for 1830,* ed. by James S. Dearden, introd. by Van Akin Burd (Aldershot and Brookfield, VT: Scolar, 1990).

Ruskin, John, *The Elements of Drawing*, ed. by Bernard Dunstan (London: Herbert, 1991).

Ruskin, John, *Fors Clavigera, I*, trans. into Japanese by Takero Isoya (Yokohama : Wild Olives Group, 1991).

Ruskin, John, *John Ruskin's Selected Writings*, ed. by Kenneth Clark (Harmondsworth: Penguin, 1991) [previously entitled *Ruskin Today*].

Ruskin, John, *The Storm Cloud of the Nineteenth Century*, trans. into Japanese by Takero Isoya (Yokohama: Wild Olives Group, 1992).

Ruskin, John, *Præterita*, ed. by A.O.J. Cockshut, Whitehouse Edition of John Ruskin (Keele: Ryburn, 1994).

Ruskin, John, *Ruskin's Letters in the Mikimoto Collection: A Facsimile Edition*, foreword by Mikio Sumiya (Tokyo: Ruskin Library of Tokyo, 1994).

Ruskin, John, *Die sieben Leuchter der Baukunst*, trans. into German by Wolfgang Kemp (Dortmund: Harenberg, 1994).

Ruskin, John, *Steine von Venedig*, trans. into German by Wolfgang Kemp, 3 vols (Dortmund: Harenberg, 1994).

Ruskin, John, *Unto this Last*, a paraphrase by M.K. Gandhi, trans. from the Gujarati by Valji Govindi, new edn (Ahmedabad: Navajivan, 1994).

Ruskin, John, *Selected Writings*, ed. by Philip Davis, Everyman Library (London: Dent, 1995).

Ruskin, John, and Effie, *John und Effie Ruskin: Briefe aus Venedig*, ed. by Wolfgang Kemp (Stuttgart: Bei Hatje, 1995).

WORKS ON RUSKIN

Adams, Edward, 'Epic History and the Novel: Gibbon, Ruskin, Adams, and the Decline and Fall of Country-House Civilization', unpublished doctoral thesis, Yale University, 1993; abstract in *Dissertation Abstracts*, 54 (1993–94), 4446-A.

Aguirre, Robert D., 'Writing Subjects: Ideology and Self-Representation in Victorian Autobiography', unpublished doctoral thesis, Harvard University, 1990; abstract in *Dissertation Abstracts*, 51 (1990–91), 2382-A.

Ameri, Amir H., '… Alberti … Laugier … Ruskin … on Natural Architecture: A Discourse on Design; or, a Discursive De-sign', unpublished doctoral thesis, Cornell University, 1988; abstract in *Dissertation Abstracts*, 49 (1988–89), 3531-A.

Anderson, Phillip B., 'Reading a Vital World: Ruskin's "The Work of Iron, in Nature, Art, and Policy"', *Publications of the Arkansas Philological Association*, 16 (1990), 1–18.

Andros, Victoria A., 'The Rev. John Eagles', *Wadham College Gazette*, n.s. 3 (1992), 30–32.

Andros, Victoria A., 'Ruskin and his Rivals: *Modern Painters* I (1843) and the Criticism of J. M. W. Turner in the Contemporary Periodical Press', unpublished doctoral thesis, University of Oxford, 1994.

Angélil, Marc, 'The Construction of a Meta-Physical Structure: Truth and Utility in Nineteenth Century Architecture', *Modulus*, 22 (1993), 26–39.

Anikin, G.V. and Mikhalskaia, N.P., *Estetika Dzhona Reskina I Angliiskaia Literatura XIX* (Moscow: Nauka, 1986).

Anon., 'The Versatile Ruskin', *Ruskin Gazette*, 1, 2 (1988), 46–66.

Anon., 'Art and History', *Ruskin Gazette*, 1, 6 (1993), 26–30.

Anon., 'John Atkinson Grimshaw (1836–93): A Contemporary of Ruskin', *Ruskin Gazette*, 1, 6 (1993), 21–25.

Anon., 'Ruskin Collection at Lancaster', *Royal Institute of British Architects Journal*, 100 (1993), 7 [on the launching of an appeal to fund a purpose-built Ruskin Library].

Anon., 'The Art of Seeing: John Ruskin and the Victorian Eye', *American Artist*, 57 (Sept. 1993), 8 [review of a travelling exhibition at the Indianapolis Museum of Art; the exhibition was also reviewed in *Drawing*, 15 (July-Aug. 1993), 36–37, when at the Phoenix Art Museum, and in *Museum News*, 72 (Mar.-April 1993), 12–13].

Atkinson, Terry, 'Phantoms of the Studio', *Oxford Art Journal*, 13 (1990), 49–62.

Austin, Linda M., 'The Art of Absence in *The Stones of Venice*', *Journal of Pre-Raphaelite Studies*, 6 (1986), 1–14.

Austin, Linda M., 'Ruskin and Rose at Play with Words', *Criticism*, 28 (1986), 409–25.

Austin, Linda M., 'John Ruskin in the Landscape of Fiction', unpublished doctoral thesis, University of Rochester, 1986; abstract in *Dissertation Abstracts*, 47 (1986–87), 905-6-A.

Austin, Linda M., '*Præterita*: In the Act of Rebellion', *Modern Language Quarterly*, 48 (1987), 42–58.

Austin, Linda M., 'Ruskin and the Ideal Woman', *South Central Review*, 4, 4 (1987), 28–39.

Austin, Linda M., 'Labor, Money, and the Currency of Words in *Fors Clavigera*', *ELH*, 56 (1989), 209–27.

Austin, Linda M., 'Painterly Perspective and Authority in Victorian Writings', *Mosaic*, 22 (1989), 71–80.

Austin, Linda M., 'Reading and the Romantics: Ruskin's *Fiction Fair and Foul*', *Studies in Romanticism*, 29 (1990), 583–601.

Austin, Linda M., *The Practical Ruskin: Economics and Audience in the Late Work* (Baltimore: Johns Hopkins University Press, 1991).

Austin, Linda M., 'Ruskin's Precritical Reading', *Victorians Institute Journal*, 19 (1991), 71–88.

Bancroft, Rose L., 'The Victorian Concept of the Italian Renaissance in Browning, Ruskin, Eliot and Pater', unpublished doctoral thesis, University of Miami, 1992; abstract in *Dissertation Abstracts*, 54 (1993–94), 184-A.

Barnes, Janet, 'Ruskin and the Mosaics of St Mark's in Venice', *Antique Collector* (Mar. 1990), 62–63.

Barnes, Janet, 'The Mineral Collection of John Ruskin in the Ruskin Gallery, Sheffield', *UK Journal of Mines and Minerals*, no. 11 (1992).

Barnes, Philip, *St. George, Ruskin and the Dragon*, The Ruskin Gallery, Collection of the Guild of St. George (Sheffield: Sheffield Arts Department, 1992).

Barrie, David, 'Religion, science and art', *Apollo*, n.s. 129 (1989), 313–16.

Bate, Jonathan, 'Wordsworth, Ruskin, and the Moral of Landscape', *Literature and Belief*, 10 (1990), 1–23.

Bate, Jonathan, *Romantic Ecology: Wordsworth and the Environmental Tradition* (London: Routledge, 1991).

Battrick, Elizabeth, *"The most active Volcano in Europe": Canon Hardwicke Drummond Rawnsley, a Founder of the National Trust* (London: National Trust, 1995).

Beatty, Michael, 'John Ruskin and the Context of *Modern Painters*', *English Studies in Africa*, 27 (1986), 27–47.

Beatty, Michael, 'A Pot of Paint in the Public's Face: Ruskin's Censure of Whistler Reconsidered', *English Studies in Africa*, 30 (1987), 27–41.

Beckett, Ruth, '"Past and Present": Carlyle and Ruskin on Scott and Victorian Medievalism' , in *Scott in Carnival*, ed. by J.H. Alexander and David Hewitt (Aberdeen: Association for Scottish Literature Studies, 1993), pp.512–22.

Beckwith, A., 'John Ruskin's Use of Illuminated Manuscripts: The Case of the Beaupré Antiphonary', *Ruskin Gazette*, 1, 1 (1987), 32–52.

Bell, Quentin, *Ruskin*, trans. into Japanese by Keiko Idebuchi (Tokyo: Shobunsha, 1989).

Bell, Quentin, *Ruskin*, trans. into Italian by Katia Lysy (Rome: Edizioni dell' Elefante, 1990).

Bell, Srilekha, 'John Ruskin: A Prophet in Transition', *Essays in Arts & Sciences*, 11 (1982), 49–57.

Bernabei, Franco, 'L'Architettura di Superficie: Venezia e la Toscana', in Clegg and Tucker (1994), pp.74–85.

Bicknell, Peter and Jane Munro, *Gilpin to Ruskin: Drawing Masters and their Manuals, 1800–1860* (Cambridge: Fitzwilliam Museum, 1987).

Birch, Dinah, *Ruskin's Myths* (Oxford: Clarendon, 1988).

Birch, Dinah, 'Ruskin's "Womanly Mind"', *Essays in Criticism*, 38 (1988), 308–24.

Birch, Dinah, '"The Sun is God": Ruskin's Solar Mythology', in *The Sun is God: Painting, Literature and Mythology in the Nineteenth Century*, ed. by J.B. Bullen (Oxford: Clarendon, 1989), pp.109–23.

Birch, Dinah, '*The Ethics of the Dust*: Ruskin's Authorities', *Prose Studies*, 12 (1989–90), 147–58.

Birch, Dinah, 'Ruskin and Tuscany', *Apollo*, n.s. 137 (March 1993), 190–91.

Birch, Dinah, 'Fathers and Sons: Ruskin, John James Ruskin and Turner' , *Nineteenth-Century Contexts*, 18 (1994), 147–62.

Birch, Dinah, 'Beauty and the Victorian Body', *Essays in Criticism*, 44 (1994), 102–16 [on Dickens, Ruskin, *et al.*].

Bizup, Joseph, 'Walter Pater and the Ruskinian Gentleman', *English Literature in Transition*, 38 (1995), 51–69.

Bloom, Harold, ed., *John Ruskin*, Modern Critical Views (New York: Chelsea, 1986).

Blythe, David-Everett., 'Ruskin, Shakespeare and the Elements of Seeing', *Kentucky Philological Review*, 2 (1987), 30–37.

Bone, J. Drummond, 'Turner and Shelley: The Sense of a Comparison', *Ruskin Gazette*, 1, 4 (1990), 30–36.

Boris, Eileen, *Art and Labor: Ruskin, Morris, and the Craftsman Ideal in America* (Philadelphia: Temple University Press, 1986).

Bosomworth, Dorothy, *Ruskin and Mosaics* (Sheffield: Sheffield Arts Department, 1990).

Bossche, Chris R. Vanden, 'The Queen in the Garden/The Woman of the Streets: The Separate Spheres and the Inscription of Gender', *Journal of Pre-Raphaelite Studies*, n.s. 1, 1 (1992), 1–15.

Boucher, Bruce, 'The Venetian scene', *Apollo*, n.s. 123 (1986), 356–57 [on exhibitions at the Palazzo Fortuny, Venice: 'Venezia nell'età di Canova' and 'Venezia nell' ottocento'].

Bradley, Alexander, *Ruskin and Italy*, Nineteenth-Century Studies series (Ann Arbor and London: University Microfilms International, 1987).

Bradley, Alexander, 'The Last Three Visits', *Ruskin Gazette*, 1, 4 (1990), 1–8.

Bradley, Alexander, 'Ruskin at Oxford: Pupil and Master', *Studies in English Literature, 1500–1900*, 32 (1992), 747–64.

Brooks, Michael, *John Ruskin and Victorian Architecture* (London: Thames, Hudson, 1989).

Brooks, Michael, 'New England Gothic: Charles Eliot Norton, Charles H. Moore and Henry Adams', *Studies in the History of Art*, 35 (1990), 113–25.

Brown, D.B., *et al.*, *The Pre-Raphaelites in Oxford* (Tokyo: Art Life, 1987).

Brown, Paula Wood, 'Sublimations of the Sublime: Boundaries of Romanticism in *Modern Painters*', unpublished doctoral thesis, University of Tennessee, 1994; abstract in *Dissertation Abstracts*, 56 (1995–96), 557-A.

Brownell, R.L., 'A Study of John Ruskin's *The Seven Lamps of Architecture* and *The Stones of Venice*', unpublished doctoral thesis, University of Essex, 1987; abstract in *Dissertation Abstracts*, 49 (1988–89), 1148-A.

Bryson, Norman, 'Enhancement and Displacement in Turner', *Huntington Library Quarterly*, 49 (1986), 47–65.

Bullen, J.B., 'Ruskin and the tradition of Renaissance historiography', in Wheeler and Whiteley (1992), pp.54–76.

Bullen, J.B. *The Myth of the Renaissance in Nineteenth-Century Writing* (Oxford: Clarendon, 1994).

Bullen, J.B., 'Ruskin, Venice and the Construction of Femininity', *Review of English Studies*, 46 (1995), 502–20.

Burd, Van Akin, *Ruskin, Lady Mount-Temple and the Spiritualists*, trans. into Japanese by Takero Isoya (Yokohama: Wild Olives Group, 1991).

Burd, Van Akin, *More Letters from Rose la Touche* (with J.S. Dearden, *The Portraits of Rose la Touche*), trans. into Japanese by Takero Isoya (Yokohama: Wild Olives Group, 1991).

Burd, Van Akin, 'Frederick James Sharp, 1880–1957: Portrait of a Bibliophile, xxxli', *Book Collector*, 44 (1995), 542–73.

Burns, Marjorie J., 'The Anonymous Fairy Tale: Ruskin's *King of the Golden River*', *Mythlore*, 14 (1988), 38–42.

Burns, Sarah, 'A pot of paint: aesthetics on trial in Whistler v. Ruskin', *Winterthur Portfolio*, 28 (1993), 105–8.

Bury, S.J., 'Past Present: John Ruskin and History', unpublished doctoral thesis, University of London, 1990.

Carrier, D., 'The Aesthete in the City', *Arts Magazine*, 64 (1990), 67–73 [on *The Stones of Venice*].

Carroll, David, 'Pollution, defilement and the art of decomposition', in Wheeler (1995), pp.58–75.

Casillo, Robert, 'The Stone Alive: Adrian Stokes and John Ruskin', *Journal of Pre-Raphaelite Studies*, 7, 1 (1986), 1–28.

Casillo, Robert, 'The Meaning of Venetian History in Ruskin and Pound', *University of Toronto Quarterly*, 55 (1985–86), 235–60.

Casillo, Robert, 'Parasitism and Capital Punishment in Ruskin's *Fors Clavigera*', *Victorian Studies*, 29 (1986), 537–67.

Casillo, Robert, 'Ruskin, Pound and the Fate of Venetian Art', *Journal of Pre-Raphaelite and Aesthetic Studies*, 1, 1 (1988), 89–109.

Casson, Sir Hugh, *The Tumbled Giant*, The Reynolds Lecture (London: Royal Academy, 1987); rpt. in *Ruskin Gazette*, 1, 2 (1988), 1–19 [on Ruskin's relationship to Venice].

Casteras, Susan P., '"The Germ of a Museum Arranged first for Workers in Iron": Ruskin's Museological Theories and the Curating of the Saint George's Museum', in Gordon and Gully (1993), pp.184–210.

Cate, George Allen, *John Ruskin: a reference guide* (Boston: Hall, 1988).

Caws, Mary Ann, *The Art of Inference: Stressed Readings in Verbal and Visual Texts* (Cambridge: Polity; Princeton: Princeton University Press, 1989).

Caws, Mary Ann, 'Against Completion: Ruskin's Drama of Dreams, Lateness and Loss', in *Sex and Death in Victorian Literature*, ed. by Regina Barreca (Houndmills and London: Macmillan, 1990), pp.107–19.

Caws, Mary Ann, 'Ruskin's Rage and Ours: The Dramatic Style', *Browning Institute Studies*, 18 (1990), 33–53.

Caws, Mary Ann, 'Cognitive Poetics and Passionate Beauty in Ruskin and Hopkins', *Rivista di Letterature Moderne e Comparate*, 44 (1991), 241–62.

Cerutti, Toni, 'La Torino di Ruskin', *Bollettino del CIRVI* (1986), 19–46.

Cerutti, Toni, '"Is Time a Sense or a Figure?": The Instability of the Ruskinian Text', in Clegg and Tucker (1994), pp.117–29.

Chierici, Renato, 'Ruskin e l'esperienza lucchese', in Clegg and Tucker (1994), pp.36–49.

Chitty, Gill, 'A Prospect of Ruins', *Association for Studies in the Conservation of Historic Buildings Transactions*, 12 (1987), 43–60.

Chitty, Gill, '"A great entail": the historic environment', in Wheeler (1995), pp.102–22.

Claridge, Gordon, Ruth Pryor, and Glen Watkins, *Sounds from the Bell Jar* (London and Houndmills: Macmillan, 1990).

Clark, Kenneth, *Introduction to Praeterita*, trans. into Japanese by Takero Isoya (Yokohama: Wild Olives Group, 1992).

Clegg, Jeanne, 'I Daguerreotipi della collezione Ruskin', *Ruskin Newsletter,* 32/33 (1986), 8–10.

Clegg, Jeanne, 'Circe and Prosperina: John Ruskin to Joan Severn, Ten Days in Sicily, 1874', *Quaderni del Dipartimento di Linguistica: Letteratura,* 2 (1986), 113–38.

Clegg, Jeanne, 'Superficial Pastimes, Fine Emotions and Metaphysical Intentions: James and Ruskin in Venice', in *Henry James e Venezia* (Florence: Olschki, 1987), pp.159–70.

Clegg, Jeanne and Paul Tucker, *Ruskin and Tuscany,* Ruskin Gallery, Collection of the Guild of St. George (Sheffield and London: Ruskin Gallery/Humphries, 1993); *Ruskin e la Toscana* (London: Humphries/La Fondazione Ragghianti, Lucca, 1993); trans. into Japanese by Takero Isoya (Yokohama: Wild Olives Group, 1994).

Clegg, Jeanne and Paul Tucker, eds., *The Dominion of Daedalus: Papers from the Ruskin Workshop held in Pisa and Lucca, 13–14 May 1993* (St Albans: Brentham/Guild of St George, 1994).

Cohn, Marjorie B./Fogg Art Museum, *Turner, Ruskin, Norton, Winthrop* (Cambridge, MA: Harvard University Art Museums, 1993).

Cole, Malcolm, *'Be Like Daisies': John Ruskin and the Cultivation of Beauty at Whitelands College,* The Ruskin Lecture, 1992 (St Albans: Brentham/Guild of St George, 1992).

Colley, Ann C., 'Mapping in and out of the Borders of Time: Ruskin and Hopkins', *Victorian Literature and Culture,* 19 (1991), 107–21.

Connelly, Frances S., 'Ruskin's True Griffin: The Relationship of Medievalism to Primitivism and the Formation of an Alternate Aesthetic', *Poetica,* 39, 40 (1993), 179–89.

Conner, Patrick, 'John Ruskin in Italy in 1845: a Voyage of Discovery', *Old Water-Colour Society's Club 62nd Annual Volume* (1991), 30–39.

Connett, Maureen, 'The Light behind the Lamps', *Traditional Homes* (1989), 85–88.

Coppen, Roger, 'Ruskin's Works Housed', *Country Life,* 8 March 1989, pp.151–52.

Corradini, Claudia Ruggiero, *Saggio su John Ruskin: il messaggio nello stile* (Florence: Olschki, 1989).

Corrigan, Maureen, 'Medievalism and the Myth of Revival in Nineteenth and Twentieth-Century Thought', unpublished doctoral thesis, University of Pennsylvania, 1987; abstract in *Dissertation Abstracts,* 49 (1988–89), 257-A [on Carlyle, Chesterton, Morris and Ruskin].

Cosgrove, Denis and Stephen Daniels, eds., *The Iconography of Landscape:Essays on the Symbolic Representation, Design and Use of Past Environments* (Cambridge: Cambridge University Press, 1988).

Cosgrove, Denis, *'Mappa mundi, anima mundi*: imaginative mapping and environmental representation', in Wheeler (1995), pp.76–101.

Costantini, Paolo, and Italo Zannier, *I Dagherrotipi della Collezzione Ruskin* (Florence: Alinari; Venice: Arsenale, 1986).

Costantini, Paolo, and Italo Zannier, *Itinerario Fiorentino: Le 'Mattinate' di Ruskin nelle fotografie degli Alinari* (Florence: Alinari, 1986).

Coyle, John, 'Proust and Ruskin: A Study in Influence', unpublished doctoral thesis, University of Glasgow, 1987.

Coyle, M. "" A Profounder Didacticism: Ruskin, Orage and Pound's Reception of Social Credit', *Paideuma*, 17 (1988), 7–28.

Crawford, Margaret, 'Arts and Crafts as an ideological myth', *Journal of Architectural Education*, 44 (Nov. 1990), 59–61.

Cronin, Richard, 'Ruskin and Colour', *Ruskin Gazette*, 1, 3 (1989), 1–8.

Crosby, Christina, 'Reading the Gothic Revival: "History" and Hints on Household Taste', in *Rewriting the Victorians: Theory, History and the Politics of Gender*, ed. by Linda M. Shires (New York: Routledge, 1992), pp.101–15 [on *The Stones of Venice* and Ruskin's relationship to Gothic Revival Architecture, Pugin and Eastlake].

Cruickshank, Dan, 'Good Godwin', *Architectural Review*, 194, 1158 (1991), 74–79.

Culver, Stuart, 'Whistler v. Ruskin: The Courts, the Public, and Modern Art', in *The Administration of Aesthetics: Censorship, Political Criticism and the Public Sphere*, ed. by Richard Burt, Cultural Politics, 7 (Minneapolis: University of Minneapolis Press, 1994).

Daley, Kenneth, 'The Rescue of Romanticism: John Ruskin and Walter Pater', unpublished doctoral thesis, New York University, 1993; abstract in *Dissertation Abstracts*, 54 (1993–94), 4100-A.

Danahay, Martin A., 'Matter out of Place: The Politics of Pollution in Ruskin and Turner', *Clio*, 21 (1991–92), 61–77.

Danahay, Martin A., *A Community of One: Masculine Autobiography and Autonomy in Nineteenth Century Britain* (Albany: State University of New York Press, 1993).

Darras, Jacques and Daniel Snowman, *Beyond the Tunnel of History* (Ann Arbor: University of Michigan Press; Basingstoke: Macmillan, 1990).

Davis, Alan, 'The Old Watercolour Society and *Modern Painters* I', *Ruskin Programme Bulletin*, no. 4 (April 1994), 5–14.

Davis, Alan, 'Ruskin, Turner, and the Pass of Faido', *Turner Society News*, no.71 (Dec. 1995), 9–12.

Davis, Philip, 'Arnold or Ruskin?', *Literature & Theology*, 6 (1992), 320–44.

Dawson, John, *John Ruskin in Coniston* (Clunton, Shropshire: Hawthorn; Coniston: Ruskin Museum, 1988).

Dawson, John, *Fourpence for the Beggar Man* (Coniston: the author, 1994).

Dearden, James S., 'Ruskin and the Blue Coat School', *Ruskin Newsletter*, 30/31 (1986), 10.

Dearden, James S., *John Ruskin's Tour of England in 1837* (Bembridge: Ruskin Galleries, 1987).

Dearden, James S., 'John James Ruskin: Artist & Patron', *Journal of Pre-Raphaelite and Aesthetic Studies*, 1, 1 (1987), 48–55.

Dearden, James S., *John Ruskin und die Schweiz* (Basle: Historisches Museum, 1988); *John Ruskin et les Alpes* (Sion: Musées Cantonaux, 1989); *John Ruskin e le Alpi* (Turin: National Mountain Museum, 1990).

Dearden, James S., 'J. Howard Whitehouse and the Ruskin Galleries at Bembridge School', in *The Island from Within*, ed. by R. Sawyer (Bembridge: Robook, 1990), pp.50–54.

Dearden, James S., *John Ruskin's Camberwell* (St Albans: Brentham/Guild of St George, 1990).

Dearden, James S., *John Ruskin: an Illustrated Life* , trans. into Japanese by Takero Isoya (Yokohama: Wild Olives Group, 1991a).

Dearden, James S., and Michael Wheeler, *John Ruskin and the Alps* (Lancaster: Lancaster University, 1991b).

Dearden, James S., *The Portraits of Rose La Touche*, trans. into Japanese by Takero Isoya (Yokohama: Wild Olives Group, 1991c).

Dearden, James S., ed., *John Ruskin and Victorian Art* (Tokyo: Tokyo Shimbun, 1993a).

Dearden, James S., 'John Ruskin and Victorian Art', in Dearden (1993a), pp.41–45.

Dearden, James S. and Jillian R. Dearden, *To Japan with Ruskin 1993* (Yokohama: Wild Olives Group, 1993) ; trans. into Japanese by Takero Isoya (Yokohama: Wild Olives Group, 1993b).

Dearden, James S., 'John Ruskin's first published work', *Book Collector*, 43 (1994), 299–300.

Dearden, James S., *Ruskin, Bembridge and Brantwood: the Growth of the Whitehouse Collection* (Keele: Ryburn, 1994).

Dearden, James S., 'The Library Edition of the Works of John Ruskin', *Book Collector*, 44 (1995), 51–66.

De Laura, D., 'Ruskin, Arnold, and Browning's Grammarian: "Crowded with Culture"', in *Victorian Perspectives: Six Essays*, ed. by John Clubbe and Jerome Meckier (Newark, N.J.: University of Delaware Press, 1989; London: Macmillan, 1989), pp.68–119.

Dellamora, Richard, 'Equivocal Images: Ruskin, Turner and Tintoretto', *Victorian Studies Association of Western Canada Newsletter*, 9 (1986), 19–20.

Dellamora, Richard, 'Revising Ruskin: The Not Quite New John Ruskin', *Newsletter of the Victorian Studies Association of Western Canada*, 13 (1987), 1–12.

Dibdin, Michael, 'Betrayed into delight', *Modern Painters*, 8 (1995), 54–55 [on *The Stones of Venice*].

Diedrick, James, 'The Sublimation of Carnival in Ruskin's Theory of the Grotesque', *Victorian Newsletter*, 74 (Fall 1988), 11–16 [includes a comparison with Bakhtin].

Dixon, Anne Campbell, 'Ruskin's Romantic Fancies', *Country Life*, 27 (1989), 130–33.

Dougherty, Charles T., 'John Ruskin', in W.B. Thesing, ed., *Victorian Prose Writers before 1867* (Detroit: Gale, 1987), pp.265–86.

Dowling, Linda, 'Ruskin's Pied Beauty and the Constitution of a "Homosexual" Code', *Victorian Newsletter*, no. 75 (Spring 1989), 1–8.

Dunlop, Robert, *Waters under the Bridge: the Saga of the La Touches of· Harristown, John Ruskin and his Irish Rose* (Kilcullen: the author, 1988).

Dwyer, Warren, 'Ruskin to the "Elusive" Mr Horn: an unpublished letter from a neglected friendship', *Victorian Newsletter*, no. 78 (1990), 14–18.

Dwyer, William, 'Ruskin at the Folger', *Nineteenth Century Prose*, 19 (1992), 73–74.

Eauclaire, Sally, 'Critical passions at the Santa Fe Opera', *Art News* (Summer 1995), 36.

Emerson, Sheila, 'The Authorization of Form: Ruskin and the Science of Chaos', in *Chaos and Order: Complex Dynamics in Literature and Science*, ed. by N. Katherine Hayles (Chicago: University of Chicago Press, 1991), pp.149–66.

Emerson, Sheila, *Ruskin: The Genesis of Invention* (Cambridge: Cambridge University Press, 1993).

Farthing, Stephen, 'Ruskin and Art Education, 1836–1992', *Review of the Pre-Raphaelite Society*, 1 (1993), 15–24.

Farthing, Stephen, 'Ruskin and Art Education', *Ruskin Gazette* 1, 7 (1994), 15–21.

Ferreira-Buckley, Linda, 'The Influence of Hugh Blair's *Lectures on Rhetoric and Belles Lettres* on Victorian Education: Ruskin and Arnold on Cultural Literacy', unpublished doctoral thesis, Pennsylvania State University, 1990; abstract in *Dissertation Abstracts* 51 (1990–91), 2024-A.

Finley, C. Stephen, 'The Structure of Ruskin's *Fors Clavigera*', *Prose Studies*, 9 (1986), 71–85.

Finley, C. Stephen, 'Ruskin, Darwin and the Crisis of Natural Form', *Cahiers Victoriens et Edouardiens*, 25 (1987), 7–24.

Finley, C. Stephen, 'Scott, Ruskin, and the Landscape of Autobiography', *Studies in Romanticism*, 26 (1988), 549–72.

Finley, C. Stephen, 'Bunyan among the Victorians: Macaulay, Froude, Ruskin', *Literature & Theology*, 3 (1989), 77–94.

Finley, C. Stephen, 'Ruskin and Mimic Engineering', *Nineteenth-Century Literature*, 44 (1989–90), 201–14.

Finley, C. Stephen, *Nature's Covenant: Figures of Landscape in Ruskin* (University Park, PA.: Pennsylvania State University Press, 1992).

Fontaney, Pierre, 'Ordre et Désordre selon Ruskin: le grotesque', *Cahiers Victoriens et Edouardiens*, 28 (1988), 7–16.

Franzini, Maurizio, '"The Political Economy of Art" di John Ruskin', in Clegg and Tucker (1994), pp.61–73.

Fraser, Hilary, *Beauty and Belief: Aesthetics and Religion in Victorian Literature* (Cambridge: Cambridge University Press, 1986).

Fraser, Hilary, *The Victorians and Renaissance Italy* (Oxford and Cambridge, MA: Blackwell, 1992).

Frick, P., 'Wilkie Collins and John Ruskin', *Victorians Institute Journal*, 13 (1987), 11–22.

Fuller, Peter, 'Ruskin today', *New Society*, 64 (1986), 352–53.

Fuller, Peter, 'The Stones of Coniston', *Independent Magazine*, 5 Nov. 1988, pp.72–75.

Fuller, Peter, *Theoria: Art, and the Absence of Grace* (London: Chatto, Windus, 1988).

Fuller, Peter, '"Black skeleton and blinding square"', in Wheeler and Whiteley (1992), pp.167–78.

Fuller, Peter, 'The Ruskin Lecture', in *Peter Fuller's Modern Painters: Reflections on British Art*, ed. by John McDonald (London: Methuen, 1993), pp.3–20.

Gamble, Cynthia, 'Ruskin and Proust', *Ruskin Gazette*, 1, 5 (1992), 1–9.

Gamble, Cynthia, 'Proust-Ruskin Perspectives on *La Vierge Dorée* at Amiens Cathedral', *Word & Image*, 9 (1993), 270–86.

Gamble, Cynthia, 'A l'ombre de la Vierge Dorée de la Cathédrale d'Amiens: Ruskin et l'imaginaire proustien', *Gazette des Beaux Arts*, n.s. 6, 125 (May-June 1995), 313–22.

Garbutt, John, *Ruskin Index: the works and associated items of John Ruskin held at the Armitt Library, Ambleside* (Ambleside: Armitt Library, 1993).

Garrigan, Kristine Ottesen, 'John Ruskin (1819–1900)', in *Victorian Britain: An Encyclopaedia*, ed. by Sally Mitchell (New York: Garland, 1988), pp.685–87.

Garrigan, Kristine Ottesen, 'Bearding the Competition: John Ruskin's *Academy Notes*', *Victorian Periodicals Review*, 22 (1989), 148–56.

Garrigan, Kristine Ottesen, 'The splendidest May number of the *Graphic*: John Ruskin and the Royal Academy Exhibition of 1875', *Victorian Periodicals Review*, 24 (1991), 22–33.

Garrigan, Kristine Ottesen, *Victorian Art Reproductions in Modern Sources: a Bibliography* (New York: Garland, 1991).

Gatens, William J., 'John Ruskin and Music', *Victorian Studies*, 30 (1986), 77–97 and 153–55, with cassette containing Ruskin's music performed by Paul Proveaux (baritone) and W.J. Gatens (piano).

Gatens, William J., 'John Ruskin and Music', in *The Lost Chord: Essays on Victorian Music*, ed. by Nicholas Temperley (Bloomington: Indiana University Press, 1989), pp.68–88.

Genette, G., 'Un de mes écrivains préférés', *Poétique*, 21 (1990), 509–19.

Gerard, David, *John Ruskin & William Morris: The Energies of Order and Love* (London: Nine Elms, 1988).

Giddey, Ernest, 'Ruskin's Debt to Rogers', *Ruskin Gazette*, 1, 5 (1992), 15–22.

Gifford, Terry, 'Conclusion', in Wheeler (1995), pp.187–94.

Glynn, Jenifer, *Prince of Publishers: a Biography of George Smith* (London: Alison, Busby, 1986).

Golby, Michael, ed., *Ruskin plus ten* (Exeter: Exeter University School of Education, 1986).

Gombrich, Sir Ernst, 'Why preserve historic buildings?: the Continued Relevance of Ruskin', *Christie's International Magazine*, Feb. 1991, pp.2–5.

Gordon, Susan Phelps, and Anthony Lacy Gully, eds., *John Ruskin and the Victorian Eye* (New York: Abrams/Phoenix Art Museum, 1993).

Gordon, Susan Phelps, 'Heartsight Deep as Eyesight: Ruskin's Aspirations for Modern Art', in Gordon and Gully (1993), pp.116–57.

Graham, D., *Gandhi's Debt to Ruskin and to Tolstoy*, trans. into Japanese by Takero Isoya (Yokohama: Wild Olives Group, 1989).

Graves, Susan, 'A Disciple of Ruskin: Frank Saltfleet (1860–1917)', *Sheffield Arts Review* (1989), 6–15.

Gravina, Michele, and Paul Tucker, 'John Ruskin's 1845 Résumé: Un ipertesto in costruzione', *Centro di Ricerche Informatiche per i Beni Culturali*, 4 (1994), 101–12.

Green, Dudley, 'The Old Man of Coniston', *Preview of Lakeland* (March 1990), 26–32.

Griffiths, Jeremy, *The De Croy Book of Hours* (Sheffield: Ruskin Gallery, 1993).

Grogan, Ruth A., 'Tomlinson, Ruskin, and Moore: Facts and Fir Trees', *Twentieth Century Literature*, 35 (1989), 183–94.

Grogan, Ruth A, 'Tomlinson, Ruskin, and Language Scepticism', *Essays in Literature*, 17 (1990), 30–42.

Gully, Anthony Lacy, 'Sermons in Stone: Ruskin and Geology', in Gordon and Gully (1993), pp.158–83.

Hackett, Lianne, 'A New Age for the Artist', *Hong Kong City Magazine*, 151 (1989), 60–66.

Haertinger, Pia, *John Ruskin und das Museum: Portrait eines Pioniers und einer Museumsepoche* (Frankfurt am Main: Lang, 1996).

Hagenbüchle, Roland and Laura Skandera, eds, *Poetry and Epistemology:Turning Points in the History of Poetic Knowledge* (Regensburg: Pustet, 1986) [on, *inter alia*, Browning, Hopkins, Ruskin and Tennyson].

Hall, Charles, 'Whistler's bother', *Arts Review*, 46 (Sept. 1994), 38–42 [on his financial troubles, and relations with critics, including Ruskin].

Hamlyn, Robin, 'An early sketchbook by J.M.W. Turner', *Record of the Art Museum (Princeton University)*, 44, 2 (1986), 2–23.

Hampsey, John C., '*The Queen of the Air*: Consistency in Ruskin's Moral Aesthetics', *McNeese Review*, 32 (1986–89), 49–57.

Hanley, Keith, 'Ruskin's Views: Gloom and Glory in Kirkby Lonsdale', in *From Lancaster to the Lakes: The Region in Literature*, ed. by Keith Hanley and Alison Milbank (Lancaster: Lancaster University Centre for North-West Regional Studies, 1992), pp.72–93.

Hanley, Keith, 'The stains of time: Ruskin and Romantic discourses of tradition', in Wheeler and Whiteley (1992), pp.98–122.

Hanley, Keith, 'In Wordsworth's Shadow: Ruskin and Neo-Romantic Ecologies', in *Influence and Resistance in Nineteenth-Century English Poetry*, ed. by K. Blank and Margot K Louis (London and Basingstoke: Macmillan, 1993), pp.203–33.

Hanley, Keith, 'The discourse of natural beauty', in Wheeler (1995), pp.10–37.

Hanson, Brian, 'Mind and Hand in Architecture: Ideas of the Artisan in English Architecture from William Chambers to John Ruskin', unpublished doctoral thesis, University of Essex, 1987; abstract in *Index to Theses* (ASLIB), 36 (1987–88), 898.

Hanson, Bruce, *Brantwood:John Ruskin's home, 1872–1900* (Coniston: Brantwood Trust, 1992).

Hanson, David C., 'Ruskin's *Præterita* and Landscape in Evangelical Children's Education', *Nineteenth-Century Literature*, 44 (1989), 45–66.

Hanson, David C., '"Out of the Same Mouth Proceedeth Blessing and Cursing": Ruskin as the "Strange Disciple"', *Modern Philology*, 90 (1992–93), 360–80.

Hardman, Malcolm, *Ruskin and Bradford: An Experiment in Victorian Cultural History* (Manchester and Dover, NH: Manchester University Press, 1986).

Hardman, Malcolm, *Six Victorian Thinkers* (Manchester: Manchester University Press, 1991).

Hark, Ina Rae, '*Unto this Last* and the Satiric Tradition', *Arnoldian*, 14 (1986–87), 21–30.

Harris, Anthony, *Why have our little girls large shoes?*, trans. into Japanese by Takero Isoya (Yokohama: Wild Olives Group, 1990).

Harris, Anthony, *Ruskin and Siena*, The Ruskin Lecture, 1991 (St Albans: Brentham/Guild of St George, 1991); trans. into Japanese by Takero Isoya (Yokohama: Wild Olives Group, 1992).

Harris, Anthony, *The Guild of St George: Two Essays*, trans. into Japanese by Takero Isoya (Yokohama: Wild Olives Group, 1992).

Harris, Anthony, 'The Guild of St George', in Clegg and Tucker (1994), pp.19–27.

Harris, Wendell, V., 'Ruskin and Pater – Hebrew and Hellene – Explore the Renaissance', *Clio*, 17 (1988–89), 173–85.

Harrod, Tanya, 'John Ruskin and the Arundel Society', *Apollo*, n.s. 127 (1988), 180–88.

Harwood, Kathleen, 'Forum: John Ruskin's Fragment of the Alps', *Drawing*, 12 (Mar.-April 1991), 129–31.

Haslam, Ray, 'Looking, Drawing and Learning with John Ruskin at the Working Mens's College', *Journal of Art & Design Education*, 7 (1988), 65–79.

Haslam, Ray, '"For the sake of the subject": Ruskin and the Tradition of Architectural Illustration', in Wheeler and Whiteley (1992), pp.138–66.

Hatton, Paul, 'Ruskin and architecture: the argument of the text', in Wheeler and Whiteley (1992), pp.123–37.

Haward, Birkin, *Oxford University Museum: its Architecture and Art* (Oxford: University Museum, 1991).

Hayman, John, 'John Ruskin's *Hortus Inclusus*: the manuscript sources and publication history', *Huntington Library Quarterly*, 52 (1989), 363–87.

Hayman, John, *John Ruskin and Switzerland* (Waterloo, Ont.: Wilfred Laurier University Press, 1991).

Hayry, H., 'The Expression of Emotion and Artistic Truth: R.G. Collingwood's Debt to the Aesthetics of John Ruskin', *Idealistic Studies*, 24 (1994), 43–52.

Heath, Lisa Marie, 'John Ruskin and Greek Art', unpublished doctoral thesis, University of Miami, 1995; abstract in *Dissertation Abstracts*, 56 (1995–96), 2693-A.

Helsinger, Elizabeth K., 'Lessons of History: Ruskin's Switzerland', in *Creditable Warriors: 1830–76*, ed. by Michael Cotsell (London: Ashfield, 1990), pp.187–208.

Helsinger, Elizabeth K., 'Ruskin and the Politics of Viewing: Constructing National Subjects', *Nineteenth-Century Contexts*, 18 (1994), 125–46.

Hempton, David, 'Popular Religion and Irreligion in Victorian Fiction', in *The Writer as Witness: Literature as Historical Evidence*, ed. by Tom Dunne (Cork: Cork University Press, 1987), pp.177–96 [on Dickens, Eliot and Ruskin].

Henderson, Heather, *The Victorian Self: Autobiography and Biblical Narrative* (Ithaca, New York: Cornell University Press, 1989), pp.65–115 [on *Præterita*].

Hewison, Robert, 'John Ruskin and the Argument of the Eye', in Gordon and Gully (1993), pp.28–51.

Hewison, Robert, *Art and Society:Ruskin in Sheffield 1876*, trans. into Japanese by Takero Isoya (Yokohama: Wild Olives Group, 1990).

Hickox, Michael, 'The Unpublished Correspondence of Ruskin and Brett', *Ruskin Gazette*, 1, 8 (1995), 1–25.

Hill, Rosemary, 'Comment: nostalgia or new wave', *Crafts*, no. 117 (July-Aug. 1992), 16–19 [on Arts & Crafts, and dealing with Ruskin and Morris].

Holland, Meridel, 'John Ruskin's Lectionary', *Durham University Journal*, 47 (1986), 301–10.

Hoyle, Peter, *Brantwood: the Story of an Obsession* (Manchester: Carcanet, 1986) [a novel].

Hunt, John Dixon, *Gardens and the Picturesque: Studies in the History of Landscape Architecture* (Cambridge, MA: Massachusetts Institute of Technology Press, 1992).

Illingworth, John, 'Ruskin and tradition: the case of museums', in Wheeler and Whiteley (1992), pp.39–53.

Illingworth, John, 'Ruskin and Gardening', *Gardening History*, 22 (1994–95), 218–33.

Isoya, Takero, *To England in pursuit of Ruskin* (Yokohama: Wild Olives Group, 1995); trans. into Japanese by the author (Yokohama: Wild Olives Group, 1995).

Jackson, Michael J., 'Psychomachia in art from Prudentius to Proust', *British Journal of Aesthetics*, 30 (Apr. 1990), 159–65.

Jackson, Michael J., 'Proust's Churches in *À la Recherche du Temps Perdu*', *Literature & Theology*, 5 (1991), 297–310.

Jackson, N., 'Tumbling to Pieces', *Country Life*, 30 (1992), 36–37.

Jenkyns, Richard, 'Ruskin and the Interpretation of Greece', *Ruskin Gazette*, 1, 3 (1989), 9–15.

Jenkyns, Richard, 'The Argument of the Eye', *Ruskin Gazette*, 1, 4 (1990), 9–17 [on descriptive prose in *Modern Painters*].

Jenkyns, Richard, 'Ruskin's Dilemma', in his *Dignity and Decadence: Victorian Art and the Classical Inheritance* (London: HarperCollins, 1991), pp.143–91.

Jespersen, Kresten, 'Form and meaning: the conventionalization of the leaf ornament', *Perspecta*, no.23 (1986), 144–55.

Jewett, Karen Elizabeth, 'Ruskin's Ministry of Taste', unpublished doctoral thesis, University of Columbia, 1993; abstract in *Dissertation Abstracts*, 54 (1993–94), 2588–89-A.

Johnson, Alan P., 'The "Scarlet Cloud": Ruskin's Revaluation of the Sixteenth Century Venetian Masters, 1858–60', *Clio*, 17 (1988–89), 151–72.

Johnson, Paul R., 'The Ideological Form of Architectural Description in John Ruskin's *Stones of Venice*', unpublished doctoral thesis, University of Wisconsin, 1990; abstract in *Dissertation Abstracts*, 51 (1990–91), 1239-A.

Johnson, Peter, 'Putting the money on Ruskin', *Sunday Times*, 7 May 1989, F3.

Jones, Stephen, 'Moral Adventure', *Country Life*, 30 April 1992, 56–57 [on exhibition 'Ruskin, Tradition and Architecture' at the Peter Scott Gallery, Lancaster University, May 1992].

Kaufman, Edward N., 'Architectural Representation in Victorian England', *Journal of the Society of Architectural Historians*, 46 (1987), 30–38.

Kawamura, Joichiro, 'Ruskin's Aesthetics', in Dearden (1993a), pp.46–56.

Keck, Stephen L., 'John Ruskin's Understanding of History: A Comparison of *The Stones of Venice* and *St Mark's Rest*', unpublished doctoral thesis, University of Oxford, 1991; abstract in *Index to Theses* (ASLIB), 42 (1993), 44.

Keefe, Robert, '"Apollo in Picardy": Pater's Monk and Ruskin's Madness', *English Literature in Transition*, 29 (1986), 361–70.

Kemp, Wolfgang, 'Die Annäherung: Motiv und Verfahren bei Ruskin und Proust', in *Marcel Proust: Motiv und Verfahren*, ed. by Edgar Mass (Frankfurt: Insel, 1986), pp.54–78.

Kemp, Wolfgang, *The Desire of my Eyes: The Life and Work of John Ruskin*, trans. from German by J. van Heurck (New York: Farrar, 1990; London: HarperCollins, 1991).

Kestner, J.A., 'Poynter and Leighton as Aestheticians: The *Ten Lectures* and *Addresses*', *Journal of Pre-Raphaelite and Aesthetic Studies*, 2, 1 (1990), 108–20.

Khambatta, Ramona, 'Ruskin and Tuscany', *Architectural Design*, 63 (May–June 1993), x–xi.

Kilgour, Margaret A., 'From Communion to Cannibalism: an Anatomy of Metaphors of Incorporation', unpublished doctoral thesis, Yale University, 1986; abstract in *Dissertation Abstracts*, 47 (1986–87), 3028-A [Chapter 5 on Coleridge, Ruskin and Melville].

Kimura, Masami, 'Ruskin's Reception in Japan and England: a Comparison', in Dearden (1993a), pp.57–67.

Kitchen, G.W., 'The Economic Basis of Ruskin's Teaching', *Ruskin Gazette*, 1, 8 (1995), 27–29

Kohane, P.M., 'Architecture, Labor and the Human Body: Fergusson, Cockerell and Ruskin', unpublished doctoral thesis, University of Pennsylvania, 1993; abstract in *Dissertation Abstracts*, 54 (1993–94), 1978-9-A.

Korte, Barbara, 'The "Femme fragile": Decline and Fall of a Literary Type', *Anglia,* 105 (1986), 366–89.

Krauss, Rosalind E., 'Une note sur l'inconscient optique', *Cahiers du Musée National d'Art Moderne*, no. 37 (1991), 60–77.

Kroll, Catherine White, 'The Self "Informed with the Infinite"; Fragmentary Representation in Friedrich Schlegel, Wordsworth, Carlyle and Ruskin', unpublished doctoral thesis, University of California, Berkeley, 1986; abstract in *Dissertation Abstracts*, 47 (1986–87), 2596-A.

Kuntz, Paul Grimley, 'The Ten Commandments of an Art-Historian – John Ruskin', *Ruskin Gazette*, 1, 7 (1994), 29–36.

Laker, Mary, *Crystal Springs: or, Rescue of Ruskin* (London: Brookside, 1992).

Lambourne, M., 'John Ruskin, John Gould and Ornithological Art', *Apollo*, n.s. 126 (1987), 185–89.

Landow, George P., *Elegant Jeremiahs: The Sage from Carlyle to Mailer* (Ithaca and London: Cornell University Press, 1986).

Landow, George P., 'Reading Pre-Raphaelite Painting', *Journal of Pre-Raphaelite and Aesthetic Studies*, 1, 1 (1988), 25–31 [on Ruskin's analysis of Tintoretto's *Annunciation*].

Landow, George P., 'How to Read Ruskin: The Art Critic as Victorian Sage', in Gordon and Gully (1993), pp.52–80.

Landow, George P., 'Ruskin', in *Victorian Thinkers*, ed. by Keith Thomas (Oxford: Oxford University Press, 1993), pp.103–92.

Lavabre, Simon, 'Ruskin, le critique d'art, témoin de son temps', in *L'Artiste, témoin de son temps*, ed. by Pierre Sahel (Provence: Université de Provence, 1990), pp.129–37.

Lawson, Julie, *The Stones of Venice: Ruskin's Venice in photographs* (Edinburgh: Scottish National Portrait Gallery, 1992).

Leith, Royal W., *Ruskin and his American Followers in Tuscany*, The Ruskin Lecture, 1994 (St Albans: Brentham Press/Guild of St George, 1994).

Leng, Andrew, 'Pater's Aesthetic Poet: The Appropriation of Rossetti from Ruskin', *Journal of Pre-Raphaelite and Aesthetic Studies*, 2, 1 (1990), 42–48.

Leonard, Diane R., 'Proust and Ruskin: Figures of Consciousness', *Style*, 22 (1988), 410–31.

Leonard, Diane R., 'Represented Space and the Poetics of Consciousness in Modernism', in *Proceedings of the XIIth Congress of the International Comparative Literature Association, 1988, Munich, V: Space and Boundaries in Literary Theory and Criticism*, ed. by Roger Bauer *et al.* (Munich: Iudicium, 1990), pp.172–78.

Leoni, Giovanni, ed., *John Ruskin, Turner e i Preraffaeliti* (Turin: Einaudi, 1992).

Le Quesne, A.L., *et al.*, *Victorian Thinkers: Carlyle, Ruskin, Arnold, Morris* (Oxford: Oxford University Press, 1993).

Levi, Donata and Paul Tucker, 'Testimonianze visive nelle conferenzi di Ruskin: i diagrams', *Ricerche di Storia dell' Arte*, 51 (1993), 85–101.

Levi, Donata, '"Drawing" *versus* "Design"', in Clegg (1994), pp.86–99.

Levinger, M., '"No Old Man's Sorrow": a new Ruskin Letter', *Burlington Magazine*, 960 (1986), 158–59.

Lew, Laurie Kane, 'Figuring a Tradition: Romantic Poetics and the Writing of English Painting, 1769–1860', unpublished doctoral thesis, University of Chicago, 1994; abstract in *Dissertation Abstracts*, 55 (1994–95), 2406-A.

Lewis, David Alan, 'Pondered Vision: The Art and Life of John Brett, A.R.A, 1830–1902', unpublished doctoral thesis, Indiana University, 1995; abstract in *Dissertation Abstracts*, 56 (1995–96), 2453-A.

Lightman, Naomi, 'The "Vulcanic dialect" in *Great Expectations*', *Dickensian*, 82 (1986), 33–38.

Lloyd, Jennifer M., 'Thunder on the Horizon: the Influence of his Historical View on the Life and Work of John Ruskin', unpublished doctoral thesis, University of Rochester, 1992; abstract in *Dissertation Abstracts*, 53 (1992–93), 596-A.

Lloyd, Jennifer M., 'Raising Lilies: Ruskin and Women', *Journal of British Studies*, 34 (1995), 325–50.

Lloyd, R.G. (Lord Lloyd of Kilgerran), 'Ruskin and the Brownings', *Ruskin Gazette*, 1, 1 (1987), 1–23.

Lloyd, R.G. (Lord Lloyd of Kilgerran), 'The Versatile Ruskin', *Ruskin Gazette*, 1, 2 (1988), 46–66.

Lloyd, R.G. (Lord Lloyd of Kilgerran), 'Ruskin: Storm Clouds of the Nineteenth Century, and the Ozone Layer of the Twentieth Century', *Ruskin Gazette*, 1, 3 (1989), 25–27.

Lloyd, R.G. (Lord Lloyd of Kilgerran), 'John Ruskin and Algernon Charles Swinburne: Prisoners of Brantwood and 2 the Pines, Putney Hill, respectively', *Ruskin Gazette*, 1, 4 (1990), 18–23.

Lloyd, R.G. (Lord Lloyd of Kilgerran), *Ruskin: Storm Clouds of the Nineteenth Century and the Ozone Layer of the Twentieth Century*, trans. into Japanese by Takero Isoya (Yokohama: Wild Olives Group, 1994).

Loucks, James F., 'Eliot's *Burbank with a Baedeker: Bleistein with a Cigar*', *ANQ* 8 (1995), 22–27 [discusses an allusion to *The Stones of Venice*].

Loughhead, C., 'Modeled Abstractions: John Ruskin and the American Modernism of Williams, Pound and Moore', unpublished doctoral thesis, Bryn Mawr College, 1985; abstract in *Dissertation Abstracts,* 47 (1986–87), 977-8-A.

Maas Gallery (London), *John Ruskin and His Circle* (London: Maas Gallery, 1991) [exhibition catalogue].

McAuley, D.I., 'Romantic critiques of industrialization and political economy in nineteenth century England', unpublished M.Phil thesis, University of Hull, 1986; abstract in *Index to Theses* (ASLIB), 37 (1988), 1342.

Macdonald, Bradley J., 'Political Theory and Cultural Criticism: Towards a Theory of Cultural Politics', *History of Political Thought,* 11 (1990), 509–29 [on the Great Exhibition of 1851 and the connection between art and politics in Carlyle, Morris and Ruskin].

MacDonald, Graham, 'The Plague Wind: John Ruskin and Dr Rae discuss the weather, 1884', *The Beaver,* 70 (1990), 44–49.

McElroy, Bernard, *Fiction of the Modern Grotesque* (New York: St Martin's, 1989) [includes the application to modern fiction of Ruskin's theories of the visual grotesque].

McGowan, John P., *Representation and Revelation: Victorian Realism from Carlyle to Yeats* (Columbia: Missouri University Press, 1986).

Machann, Clinton, 'Edward Gibbon's *Memoirs of my Life* and the Genre of Autobiography in Victorian England', *Prose Studies,* 12 (1989), 25–43.

McHugh, Fionnuala, 'Threads of History', *Telegraph Magazine,* 10 Oct. 1992, pp.56–59 [on Ruskin's May Queens at Whitelands College].

McIntosh, R.K., 'Venice Revised: John Ruskin's Venice in 1849–52 and 1876–77', unpublished doctoral thesis, University of Cambridge, 1992; abstract in *Index to Theses* (ASLIB), 42 (1993), 35.

McLaughlin, Elizabeth T., 'Metamorphosis through Words' [Chapter 1 of her *Ruskin and Gandhi*], trans. into Japanese by Takero Isoya (Yokohama: Wild Olives Group, 1989).

Madden, O.E., 'Ruskin and Oxford', *Ruskin Gazette*, 1, 1 (1987), 67–88.

Madden, O.E., 'Kindred Spirits', *Ruskin Gazette,* 1, 4 (1990), 24–29 [a comparison of Ruskin and Byron].

Madden, O.E., 'A Critical Year: The Impact of Turin', *Ruskin Gazette*, 1, 5 (1992), 23–29.

Madden, O.E., 'Ruskin in a Legal Action', *Ruskin Gazette*, 1, 6 (1993), 31–37.

Mahlis, Kristen Helen, '"Formed for Labour, not for Love": Self-cultivation and the Victorian Heroine', unpublished doctoral thesis, University of California, Berkeley, 1994; abstract in *Dissertation Abstracts*, 55 (1994–95), 2842–A [on the influence of German philosophy on the Bildungsroman and the role of Ruskin and others in drawing on this tradition to contribute to the context in which Victorian novelists wrote].

Maidment, Brian, 'Reading Ruskin and Ruskin's Readers', *PN Review*, 14 (1988), 50–53.

Malleson, M.L., 'John Ruskin: his theology and faith', unpublished MA thesis, University of Durham, 1992; abstract in *Index to Theses* (ASLIB), 45 (1996), 92.

Mallett, Phillip, 'John Ruskin: Masters and Men', in *Annales du Gerb,* 3 (1988), 91–105.

Mallett, Phillip, 'The city and the self', in Wheeler (1995), pp.38–57.

Mander, R. 'The Relationship of John Ruskin and Dante Gabriel Rossetti', *Ruskin Gazette*, 1, 1 (1987), 60–66.

Manno, Antonio, 'Appunti di viaggio: Ruskin fotografo', *Casabella*, 50 (Sept. 1986), 40 [on an exhibition at Palazzo Rucellai, Florence].

Marsh, Jan, *Elizabeth Siddal, 1829–1862: Pre-Raphaelite Artist*, The Ruskin Gallery, Collection of the Guild of St. George (Sheffield: Sheffield Arts Department, 1991).

Marsh, Jan, '"Resolve to be a Great Paintress": Women Artists in Relation to John Ruskin as Critic and Patron', *Nineteenth-Century Contexts*, 18 (1994), 177–85.

Marsh, John, 'A Fairy Story Retold: Ruskin linen and lace', *Cumbria* (March 1989), 731–32.

Marucci, Franco, 'Ruskin, Pater e il Rinascimento Sfaccettato', in Clegg and Tucker (1994), 130–42.

Mateo Sevilla, Matilde, 'La Vision Britanica del Arte Medieval Cristiano en Espana', unpublished doctoral thesis, University of Santiago de Compostela, 1994; abstract in *Dissertation Abstracts*, 56 (1995–96), 807–C.

Matthew, H.C.G., 'Hobson, Ruskin and Cobden', in Michael Freeden, ed., *Reappraising J.A. Hobson: Humanism and Welfare* (London: Unwin Hyman, 1990), pp.11–30.

Maxwell, Catherine, 'Sensitive Plants: Shelley's Influence on Ruskin', *Durham University Journal,* n.s. 56 (1995), 31–41.

Measham, Donald, 'John Ruskin presents Rose La Touche with a drawing poem', *Staple 13 New Writing* (Summer 1988), 26–27.

Measham, Donald, *John Ruskin, the Last Chapter: a Study of John Ruskin's Autobiography 'Præterita'*, The Ruskin Gallery, Collection of the Guild of St George (Sheffield: Sheffield Arts Department, 1989).

Merrill, Linda, *A Pot of Paint: Aesthetics on Trial in Whistler v Ruskin,* (Washington: Smithsonian Institution, 1992).

Merrill, Lynn L., 'Burroughs and Ruskin – "The More and Fresher Facts the Better"', in her *The Romance of Victorian Natural History* (New York and Oxford: Oxford University Press, 1989), pp.138–62.

Michalson, Karen A., 'Victorian Fantasy Literature and the Politics of Canon-Making', unpublished doctoral thesis, University of Massachusetts, 1990 ; abstract in *Dissertation Abstracts,* 51 (1990–91), 2755-A [on Ruskin, Haggard, Kingsley, Kipling and McDonald].

Michelini, C., 'From the Lessons of Ruskin to the Excavations at the Forum', *Ricerche di Storia dell' Arte,* 50 (1993), 53–61.

Milbank, Alison, 'Ruskin and Dante: Centrality and De-centring', *Bulletin of the John Rylands Library,* 73 (1991), 119–34.

Milbank, Alison, 'Ruskin and tradition : the case of French Gothic', in Wheeler and Whiteley (1992), pp.18–38.

Miller, J. Hillis, 'Catachresis, Prosopoeia, and the Pathetic Fallacy: the Rhetoric of Ruskin', in *Poetry and Epistemology: Turning Points in the History of Poetic Knowledge,* ed. by Roland Hagenbuchle and Laura Skanders (Regensburg: Pustet, 1986), pp.398–407.

Miller, J. Hillis, '*Præterita* and the Pathetic Fallacy', in *Victorian Connections,* ed. by Jerome J. McGann, Victorian Studies series (Charlottesville: University Press of Virginia, 1989), pp.172–78.

Miller, J. Hillis, 'Prosopopoeia and *Præterita*', in *Nineteenth-Century Lives: Essays Presented to Jerome Hamilton Buckley,* ed. by Laurence S. Lockridge, *et al.* (Cambridge: Cambridge University Press, 1989), pp.125–39.

Mitchell, W.R., 'Earnest Knipe: Memories of Old Lakeland', *Cumbria* (June 1987), 163–66.

Mitchell, W.R. 'Through the Years at Brantwood', *Cumbria* (Sept. 1987), 356–59.

Mitchell, W.R. 'Collingwood in Reykjavik', *Cumbria* (Jan. 1989), 594–97.

Moore, John David, 'Prelection, Prophecy, and Persuasion: The Rhetorical Development of John Ruskin as a Victorian Sage', unpublished doctoral thesis, University of Washington, 1987; abstract in *Dissertation Abstracts,* 46 (1985–66), 1951-A.

Morazzoni, Marta, *L'invenzione della verità* (Milan: Longanesi, 1988).

Morgan, Peter, 'Ruskin's *Queen of the Air*', in *Poetics of the Elements in the Human Condition, II: The Airy Elements in Poetic Imagination,* ed. by A.-T. Tymieniecke (Dordrecht: Kluwer, 1988), pp.301–8.

Morgan, Peter, F., *The Poetic and Pictorial Elements in Works by Five Writers in English: Milton, Pope, Wordsworth, Ruskin and Pound* (Lampeter: Mellen, 1992).

Müllenbrock, Heinz-Joachim, 'Literatur als Politik: zur Funktion imperialistischer Lyrik im Viktorianischen England', *Anglia,* 110 (1991), 119–42.

Munn, Geoffrey C., 'Lost Jewels', *The Magazine Antiques,* 136 (1989), 826–33 [on jewellry, and referring to Ruskin and Burne-Jones].

Munzell, Uli, 'Die Badener Zeichnungen des John Ruskin', *Badener Neujahrsblätter* (1987), 105–13.

Nagaze, Gyoro, *From Brantwood to Yasnaya Polyana,* trans. into Japanese by Takero Isoya (Yokohama: Wild Olives Group, 1996).

Neal, Patricia Anne, 'John Ruskin as Paradigm, the Creator of the modern signed Art Review', unpublished doctoral thesis, University of Texas at Austin, 1986; abstract in *Dissertation Abstracts,* 47 (1986–87), 3436-A.

Nelson, Bernadette, 'Ruskin's "Fairy Cathedrals"', *The Ashmolean,* 21 (Christmas 1991), 12–14.

Nevins, Deborah, 'Morris, Ruskin, and the English Flower Garden', *Antiques,* 129 (1986), 1256–65.

Newall, Christopher, 'Ruskin and the English watercolour', *Apollo,* n.s. 130 (1989), 267–68.

Newall, Christopher, '"The Innocence of the Eye": Ruskin and the Landscape Watercolor', in Wilcox and Newall (1992), pp.29–40.

Newall, Christopher, 'Ruskin and the Art of Drawing', in Gordon and Gully (1993), pp.81–115.

Nord, Deborah Epstein, 'Mill and Ruskin on the Woman Question Revisited', in *Teaching Literature: What is needed now,* ed. by James Engell and David Perkins (Cambridge, MA: Harvard University Press, 1988), pp.73–83.

Norwich, John Julius (Viscount Norwich), 'Preserving a Visionary's Lake District Retreat', *Architectural Digest,* 52, 1 (1995), 44.

Nugent, Charles, 'Ruskin and the Lake District', *Watercolours, Drawings and Prints,* 6, 4 (Autumn 1991), 4–7.

O'Gorman, Francis, '"Of Chains and Chequers": Charles Darwin and Ruskin's Late Science', *Ruskin Gazette,* 1, 5 (1992), 10–14.

O'Gorman, Francis, 'Ruskin's Late Science', unpublished doctoral thesis, University of Oxford, 1994; abstract in *Index to Theses* (ASLIB), 45 (1996), 92.

O'Gorman, Francis, 'A Blakean Allusion in Ruskin's *Fors Clavigera*', *Notes & Queries,* n.s. 42 (1995), 175–76.

Ostermark-Johansen, Lene, '"It's Art's Decline, My Son" – John Ruskin and Robert Browning: Two Victorian Views on the Italian Renaissance', *Angles on the English Speaking World,* 5 (1991), 35–37.

Payne, Elizabeth.E., 'John Ruskin's Romantic Idealism and its Influence on early Arts and Crafts Institutions in the Southern Appalachians', unpublished doctoral thesis, Florida State University, 1991; abstract in *Dissertation Abstracts,* 52 (1991–92), 1993-A.

Peattie, Roger W., 'Ruskin's August 1870 Letter to D.G. Rossetti', *Notes & Queries,* 33 (1986), 173–74.

Peattie, Roger W., '"Pain to Surviving Relatives": Another Defence of Effie Millais', *Journal of Pre-Raphaelite and Aesthetic Studies,* 1, 1 (1988), 75–79.

Peltason, T., 'Ruskin's Finale: Vision and Imagination in *Præterita*', *ELH,* 57 (1990), 665–84.

Pendleton, William Glen, 'Title as Epitaph: Preterition in John Ruskin's Autobiography', *CEA Critic*, 53, 1 (1990–91), 16–28.

Penny, Nicholas, *Ruskin's Drawings in the Ashmolean Museum* (Oxford: Ashmolean Museum, 1988); rpt. as *Ruskin's Drawings* (Phaidon Christie's/Ashmolean Museum, 1989).

Perry, C.J., 'A Voice of the Past: Ruskin's Pervasive Presence in Gissing's *The Odd Woman*', *Publications of the Missouri Philological Association*, 13 (1988), 63–70.

Peterson, Linda H., *Victorian Autobiography: The Tradition of Self Interpretation* (New Haven and London: Yale University Press, 1986).

Pevsner, Nikolaus, *Ruskin and Viollet-le-Duc: Englishness and Frenchness in the Appreciation of Gothic architecture*, Walter Neurath Memorial Lecture, trans. into Japanese by H. Suzuki (Tokyo: Chuo-Koron Bijutsu Shuppan, 1990).

Pfordresher, John, 'Chesterton on Browning's Grotesque', *English Language Notes*, 24, 3 (1986–87), 42–51 [on Chesterton's criticism of Browning compared to Ruskin].

Pillinini, Stefano, 'Alcune lettere "Veneziane" inedite di John Ruskin', *Archivio Veneto, V*, 127 (1986), 91–101.

Phillips, David, 'Ruskin, a growth industry', *Museums Journal*, 91 (Oct. 1991), 13.

Porterfield, Susan A., 'Love and Work: Ruskin, Mill, Dickens, Eliot', unpublished doctoral thesis, University of Northern Illinois, 1986; abstract in *Dissertation Abstracts*, 47 (1986–87), 2599-A.

Potts, Alex., 'Like the face of the moon', *Burlington Magazine*, 131 (July 1991), 473–75 [on travelling exhibition at Glynn Vivian Art Gallery, Swansea].

Powell, Kenneth, 'John Ruskin and Today's Architects', *Ruskin Gazette*, 1, 3 (1989), 28–29.

Proust, Marcel, *On Reading Ruskin: Prefaces to* La Bible d'Amiens *and* Sésame et les Lys, *with selections from the notes to translated texts*, ed. and trans. by Jean Autret, William Burford and Phillip J. Wolfe (New Haven: Yale University Press, 1987).

Rabb, Jane M., *Literature and Photography Interactions, 1840–1990* (Albuquerque: University of New Mexico Press, 1995).

Read, Richard, '"A name that makes it looked after": Turner, Ruskin and the Visual-Verbal Sublime', *Word & Image*, 5 (1989), 315–25.

Richards, Bernard, 'The Authorship of Something on Ruskinism', *Ruskin Gazette*, 1, 4 (1990), 37–44.

Richards, Bernard, 'Pater and Architecture', in Laurel Brake and Ian Small, eds., *Pater in the 1990s* (Greensboro: ELT Press, 1991), pp.189–204 [includes an extended discussion of Ruskin].

Richards, Bernard, 'Ruskin and Conservation', *Ruskin Gazette*, 1, 6 (1993), 5–20.

Richards, Bernard, 'The Impact of Rome', *Ruskin Gazette*, 1, 8 (1995), 31–35.

Richards, Jeffrey, 'The role of the railways', in Wheeler (1995), pp.123–43.

Richardson, J.F., 'The Missing Element', *Ruskin Gazette*, 1, 3 (1989), 30–32 [on *The Elements of Drawing*].

Roberts, Barbara A., 'Ruskin's Voice of Authority', unpublished doctoral thesis, University of Alabama, 1985; abstract in *Dissertation Abstracts*, 46 (1985–86), 3362-A.

Roberts, N., 'Our Kingsley', *Turner Society News*, no. 46 (November 1987), 8–10.

Rogal, Owen Shane, 'Formal Necessities and Furious Temptations in John Ruskin's *Modern Painters*', unpublished doctoral thesis, Rutgers University, 1985; abstract in *Dissertation Abstracts,* 47 (1986–87), 190-A.

Rogal, Owen Shane, 'Ruskin reading Turner's *The Slave Ship*', *Prose Studies*, 15 (1992), 49–60.

Rogal, Owen Shane, 'Morbid and Fearful Conditions of Mind in Ruskin's *Modern Painters* II', *Victorian Newsletter*, no. 85 (1994), 9–13.

Rogers, Louise, 'The Bones of Venice', *Royal Institute of British Architects Journal* (Jan. 1994), 24–29 [on plans for the new Ruskin Library at Lancaster University].

Rosenberg, John D., 'Reading the World: Visual Imagination in Dickens and Ruskin', *Arnoldian*, 2, 1 (1984), 5–13.

Rotily, Jocelyne, 'Bernard Berenson et Marcel Proust', *Gazette des Beaux Arts*, n.s. 6, 115 (Jan. 1990), 45–52.

Ruston, James H., *Ruskin pottery*, 2nd edn (Sandwell: Sandwell Metropolitan Borough Council, 1990).

Saler, Michael Theodore, 'Medieval Modernism: the Legitimation and social function of Modern Art in England, 1910–1945', unpublished doctoral thesis, Stanford University, 1992: abstract in *Dissertation Abstracts*, 53 (1992–93), 2511–A.

Sawyer, Paul, 'Ruskin and the Matriarchal Logos', in *Victorian Sages and Cultural Discourse: Renegotiating Gender and Power*, ed. by Thais E. Morgan (New Brunswick: Rutgers University Press, 1990), pp.129–41.

Sdegno, Emma, 'Reading the Painting's Suggestiveness', in Clegg and Tucker (1994), pp.100–14.

Seaton, B., 'Considering the Lilies: Ruskin's *Proserpina* and other Victorian Flower Books', *Victorian Studies*, 28 (1987), 255–82.

Sewell, Brian, 'After Claude', *Art Review,* 45 (Feb. 1994), 14–19 [on Lorrain's influence and critical reception].

Shaw, George Bernard, *Ruskin's Politics*, trans. into Japanese by Takero Isoya (Yokohama: Wild Olives Group, 1989).

Shaw, Roy, *The Relevance of Ruskin,* The Ruskin Lecture, 1987 (London: Brentham/ Guild of St George, 1988); trans. into Japanese by Takero Isoya (Yokohama: Wild Olives Group, 1990).

Shefer, Elaine, 'Elizabeth Siddal's *Lady of Shalott*', *Woman's Art Journal*, 9 (1988), 21–29.

Shuman, Cathy Elizabeth, 'Different for Girls: Gender and Professional Authority in Mill, Ruskin and Dickens', unpublished doctoral thesis, Yale University, 1994; abstract in *Dissertation Abstracts*, 55 (1994–95), 1971–2-A.

Smith, Lindsay, 'The Enigma of Visibility: Theories of Visual Perception in the early Poetry of William Morris and in the Work of Ruskin and the Pre-Raphaelites', unpublished doctoral thesis, University of Southampton, 1989; abstract in *Dissertation Abstracts*, 50 (1989–90), 3964–5-A.

Smith, Lindsay, *Victorian Photography, Painting and Poetry: The Enigma of Visibility in Ruskin, Morris and the Pre-Raphaelites* (Cambridge: Cambridge University Press, 1995).

Somboon, Vira, 'Progress and Harmony in Modern Politics: The Case of John Stuart Mill and John Ruskin', unpublished doctoral thesis, University of Michigan, 1987: abstract in *Dissertation Abstracts,* 48 (1987–88), 1533-A.

Sotheby's, *Works by Artists in the circle of John Ruskin* (London: Sotheby, 1990) [sale catalogue].

Stanford, Derek, 'England's Greatest Art Critic', *Contemporary Review,* 250 (May 1987), 267–69.

Steege, Gwen W., 'The Book of Plans and the early Romanesque revival in the United States: a study in architectural patronage', *Journal of the Society of Architectural Historians,* 46 (1987), 215–27.

Steel, David, 'Charles Dickens, John Ruskin and the old King's Arms Royal Hotel, Lancaster, with seven Letters to its Landlord, Mr. Joseph Sly', in *From Lancaster to the Lakes: The Region in Literature,* ed. by Keith Hanley and Alison Milbank (Lancaster: Lancaster University Centre for North-West Regional Studies, 1992), pp.41–58.

Stein, R.L., 'Milk, Mud and Mountain Cottages: Ruskin's Poetry of Architecture', *Publications of the Modern Language Association of America,* 100 (1987), 328–41.

Stoddart, Judith, 'Ruskin and Swinburne', *Ruskin Newsletter,* 32/33 (1986), 5–6.

Stoddart, Judith, 'The Rhetoric of Reform: John Ruskin's *Fors Clavigera* and the Politics of the 1870s', unpublished doctoral thesis, University of Oxford, 1990; abstract in *Dissertation Abstracts,* 53 (1992–93), 3541-A.

Stoddart, Judith, 'The Formation of the Working Classes: John Ruskin's *Fors Clavigera* as a Manual of Cultural Literacy', *Bucknell Review,* 34, 2 (1990), 43–58.

Stoddart, Judith, 'Ruskin's St George and the Cult of Community', *Victorians Institute Journal,* 20 (1992), 230–59.

Stoddart, Judith, 'The Morality of Poems and Ballads: Swinburne and Ruskin', in *The Whole Music of Passion: New Essays on Swinburne,* ed. by Rikky Rooksby and Nicholas Shrimpton (Aldershot: Scolar; Brookfield VT: Ashgate, 1993), pp.92–106.

Stoddart, Judith, 'Conjuring the "Necromantic Evidence" of History: Ruskin and the Enlightenment Revival of the 1870s', *Nineteenth Century-Contexts,* 18 (1994), 163–76.

Strong, Sherry Gay, 'The Mythic Framework of John Ruskin's Modern Painters', unpublished doctoral thesis, University of Iowa, 1987; abstract in *Dissertation Abstracts,* 48 (1987–88), 1780-A.

Stuart, Barbara Lawlor, 'A Hangman, a Centaur, and a Madman: Dickens' Grotesques and the Grotesque Novels', unpublished doctoral thesis, Emory University, 1988; abstract in *Dissertation Abstracts,* 50 (1989–90), 150-A [argues that Ruskin's concept of the grotesque helps to define that of Dickens].

Sumiya, Mikio, *Ryuzo Mikimoto Collection: Catalogue of the Books of the Ruskin Library* (Tokyo: Ruskin Library, 1986).

Sumner, Ann, *Ruskin and the English Watercolour from Turner to the Pre-Raphaelites* (Manchester: Whitworth Art Gallery, 1989).

Sumner, Ann, 'John Ruskin, collector of Turner watercolours', *Antique Collector* (June 1989), 90–101.

Sutton, Denys, 'Venezia, cara Venezia', *Apollo,* n.s. 125 (1987), 42–51 [preface reprinted from an exhibition catalogue on artists in Venice in the nineteenth century, Wildenstein's, London, 1972].

Swann, Charles, 'Dickens, Ruskin and the City: Parallels or Influence?', *The Dickensian,* 82, 2 (1986), 67–81.

Swann, Charles, 'Reading the Signs of the Times: Some Functions of Criticism, Arnold and Ruskin', in *Matthew Arnold: Between Two Worlds,* ed. by R. Giddings (London:Vision, 1986), pp.44–74.

Swenarton, Mark, *Artisans and Architects: the Ruskinian Tradition in Architectural Thought* (Basingstoke and London: Macmillan; New York: St Martin's, 1989).

Tanner, Tony, 'Proust, Ruskin, James and "le désir de Venise"', *Journal of American Studies,* 21 (1987), 5–29.

Tanner, Tony, *Venice Desired* (Oxford: Blackwell, 1992) [Chapter 3 : 'John Ruskin: this sea-dog of towns'].

Taylor, M., 'The Idea of Knowledge in the Development of Cultural Criticism in the Nineteenth Century, with particular reference to Carlyle, Ruskin and Arnold', unpublished doctoral thesis, Birkbeck College, University of London, 1986; abstract in *Index to Theses* (ASLIB), 36 (1987–88), 22.

Taylour, Simon, 'Ruskin, John Brett and the Val d'Aosta', *Ruskin Gazette,* 1, 3 (1989), 34–38.

Thompson, Jon, *The Guild of St George,* with Ruskin's letter on *A Scheme for St George's Museum,* and *Communism and Art: A Talk at the Walkeley Museum,* trans. into Japanese by Takero Isoya (Yokohama: Wild Olives Group, 1990).

Tiernan, M.L, 'Aesthetic Autonomy and Discursive Practice', unpublished doctoral thesis, University of Pittsburgh, 1992; abstract in *Dissertation Abstracts,* 54 (1993–94), 537-A.

Titlebaum, Richard, 'The Moralist: John Ruskin and the Italian Renaissance', in *Three Victorian Views of the Italian Renaissance,* Harvard Dissertations in American and English Literature (New York: Garland, 1987).

Tomlin, E.W.F., 'The Philosophy of Ruskin', *Arts Review,* 39 (July 1987), 506–7 [extracts from a lecture to the Royal Society at the Italian Institute, London].

Tomlin, E.W.F., 'John Ruskin: His Philosophy and Thought', *Ruskin Gazette,* 1, 2 (1988), 20–41.

Trela, D.J., 'A Lost Half-Letter of Carlyle to Ruskin surfaces', *ANQ,* 8, 2 (1995), 9–11.

Tucker, Paul, see Levi (1993).

Tucker, Paul, see Clegg (1993).

Tucker, Paul, see Clegg (1994).

Tucker, Paul, see Gravina (1994).

Tucker, Paul, 'Le Toscane di Ruskin, 1840–1882', in Clegg and Tucker (1994).

Usherwood, N., '"The Things of St George": John Ruskin at Abbot Hall, Kendal', *Country Life*, 174 (1986), 524–25.

Vaughan, William, 'The Englishness of British Art', *Oxford Art Journal*, 13, 2 (1990), 11–23.

Veyriras, Paul, 'Sainte Elisabeth de Hongrie: héroïne victorienne?', *Cahiers Victoriens et Edouardiens*, 23 (1986), 3–15.

Villari, Enrica, 'Strategies of Contradiction in *Fiction, Fair and Foul'*, in Clegg and Tucker (1994), pp.143–52.

Voon, Hye-Joon, 'Ruskin's Gothic', *The Journal of English Language and Literature*, 38, 4 (1992), 701–13.

Wagner, Virginia L, 'John Ruskin and Artistic Geology in America', *Winterthur Portfolio*, 23 (1988), 151–67.

Walmsley, R., 'The Notion of Aggressivity in *Modern Painters* I & II and *Stones of Venice* I–III', *Ruskin Newsletter*, 32/33 (1986), 4–5.

Walsh, Susan Ann, 'Ruskin's "Many-Towered City": Fragmentation and Unity in the Later Works', unpublished doctoral thesis, Duke University, 1988; abstract in *Dissertation Abstracts*, 49 (1988–89), 2235-A.

Walsh, Susan Ann, 'Ruskin's *Præterita* and the Mediated Self', *Victorians Institute Journal*, 19 (1991), 41–70.

Walton, John K., 'The National Trust: preservation or provision?', in Wheeler (1995), 144–64.

Wardle, Peter and Cedric Quayle, *Ruskin and Bewdley* (St Albans: Brentham Press/Guild of St. George, 1989).

Warner, Malcolm, *The Pre-Raphaelites in Context* (San Marino: Huntington Library, 1992).

Warrell, Ian, *Through Switzerland with Turner* (London: Tate Gallery, 1995).

Warren, C., 'John Ruskin and the Alpine Scene', *Ruskin Gazette*, 1, 1 (1987), 53–59.

Warren, C., 'Ruskin the Artist', *Ruskin Gazette*, 1, 2 (1988), 42–45.

Waterfield, Giles, ed., *Art for the People: Culture in the Slums of Late Victorian Britain* (London: Dulwich Picture Gallery, 1994).

Weinberg, Gail S., 'Ruskin, Pater, and the rediscovery of Botticelli', *Burlington Magazine*, 129 (Jan. 1987), 25–27.

Weinberg, Gail S., '"First of all first beginnings": Ruskin's studies of early Italian paintings at Christ Church', *Burlington Magazine*, 134 (Feb. 1992), 111–20.

Weingarden, Lauren S., 'Naturalized Nationalism: A Ruskinian Discourse on the Search for an American Style of Architecture', *Winterthur Portfolio*, 24, 1 (1989), 43–68.

Weiss, Theodore, 'At the Mercy of the Play: Poetry and Its Discontents', *TriQuarterly*, 73 (1988), 166–83 [on Ruskin's theories of poetry, and the pathetic fallacy].

Weltman, Sharon Aronofsky, 'Gender and the Architectonics of Metaphor: Ruskin's Pathetic Fallacy in *The Ethics of the Dust*', *Prose Studies*, 16, 2 (1993), 41–61.

Weltman, Sharon Aronofsky, 'John Ruskin and the Mythology of Gender'; unpublished doctoral thesis, Rutgers University, 1992; abstract in *Dissertation Abstracts,* 53 (1992–93), 1929–30-A.

Wettlaufer, Alexandra Ker, 'Envisioning Visionaries: the Visual Impulse in Prose from Diderot to Ruskin', unpublished doctoral thesis, Columbia University, 1993; abstract in *Dissertation Abstracts,* 54 (1993–94), 2570-A.

Wheeler, Michael, 'Ruskin and Racism', *Quarto: Abbot Hall Art Gallery Quarterly Bulletin,* 29 (1991), 25–27.

Wheeler, Michael, 'The Stones of Lancaster', *Art Quarterly,* 5 (1991), 46–49.

Wheeler, Michael, see Dearden (1991b).

Wheeler, Michael, *Ruskin's Lamps of Memory,* Inaugural Lecture (Lancaster: Lancaster University, 1991).

Wheeler, Michael, and Nigel Whiteley, eds., *The Lamp of Memory: Ruskin, Tradition and Architecture* (Manchester: Manchester University Press, 1992).

Wheeler, Michael, 'Introduction', 'Ruskin among the ruins: tradition and the temple', and 'Introductory Note on "The Lamp of Memory"', in Wheeler and Whiteley (1992), pp.1–17, 77–97, 213–14.

Wheeler, Michael, *et al., Ruskin, Tradition and Architecture* (Lancaster: Lancaster University, 1992) [catalogue of an exhibition at the Peter Scott Gallery, Lancaster University, May 1992].

Wheeler, Michael, 'John Ruskin', in *A Companion to Aesthetics,* ed. by David E. Cooper (Oxford and Cambridge, MA: Blackwell, 1992), pp.372–74.

Wheeler, Michael, 'Carlyle and Ruskin', *Carlyle Society Papers,* n.s. 7 (1993–94), 2–13.

Wheeler, Michael, 'Introduction', *Nineteenth-Century Contexts,* 18 (1994), 113–23 [special issue on Ruskin].

Wheeler, Michael, *Ruskin's Museums and Galleries: The Treasury, the Storehouse and the School – A Lecture delivered at the National Gallery, London, 21 November 1994* (London: Pilkington, 1994).

Wheeler, Michael, ed., *Ruskin and Environment: The Storm Cloud of the Nineteenth Century* (Manchester and New York: Manchester University Press, 1995a).

Wheeler, Michael, 'Introduction' and 'Environment and apocalypse', in Wheeler (1995a), pp.1–9, 165–86.

Wheeler, Michael, *Wordsworth, Rydal and Victorian Literature* (Ambleside: Armitt Trust/ Rydal Church, 1995b).

Whellens, Arthur, '"A Tuscan Sybil": a Note on Beatrice di Pian degli Ontani', in Clegg and Tucker (1994), pp.50–57.

Whiteley, Nigel, see Wheeler and Whiteley (1992).

Whiteley, Nigel, '"Falsehood in a Ciceronian dialect"? : the "Ruskinian" tradition, Modernism, and the rise of the classical tradition in contemporary architecture', in Wheeler and Whiteley (1992), pp.179–212.

Whittingham, Selby, 'Ruskin and Turner's Will', *Ruskin Gazette,* 1, 1 (1987), 24–31.

Whittingham, Selby, 'Why did Ruskin resign as Turner's Executor?', *Ruskin Gazette,* 1, 4 (1990), 45–47.

Whittingham, Selby, 'Ruskin and Turner', *Times Literary Supplement*, 22 Feb. 1991, p.13.

Wilcock, John, 'Ruskin and Mercantile Economics', *Ruskin Gazette*, 1, 7 (1994), 9–14.

Wilcox, Joel F., 'Tomlinson and the British Tradition', in *Charles Tomlinson: Man and Artist*, ed. by Kathleen O'Gorman (Columbia: University of Missouri Press, 1988), pp.41–56 [on Tomlinson's treatment of the Garden of Eden, with reference to his sources in Ruskin and Wordsworth].

Wilcox, Scott and Christopher Newall, *Victorian Landscape Watercolors* (New York: Hudson Hills/Yale Center for British Art, 1992).

Wildsmith, Claire, *Ruskin, Rawnsley and the National Trust: a display of books to celebrate the Centenary of the Founding of the National Trust* (Lancaster University: Ruskin Programme, 1995).

Wilmer, Clive, 'Minerals from the collection of John Ruskin', in his *Of Earthly Paradise* (Manchester: Carcanet, 1992), p.21 [poem].

Wilmer, Clive, 'Back to Nature: Ruskin's aspen and an art in the service of the given', *Times Literary Supplement*, 1 Dec. 1995, pp.3–4 [review article].

Wilton, Andrew and Anne Lyles, *The Great Age of British Watercolours, 1750–1880* (London: Royal Academy of Arts; Washington, DC: National Gallery of Arts, 1992).

Witemeyer, Hugh, '"Of King's Treasures": Pound's Allusion to Ruskin in Hugh Selwyn Mauberley', *Paideuma*, 15 (1986), 23–31.

Wood, Andelys, 'Above Ruskin's Labyrinth', *Victorian Newsletter*, 74 (Fall 1988), 33–37 [on *Fors Clavigera*].

Workman, Leslie J., '"My First Real Tutor": John Ruskin and Charles Eliot Norton', *New England Quarterly*, 62 (1989), 572–86.

Yokoyama, Chiaki, 'Complexities and Contradictions of Medievalism in Victorian England: Ruskin and Morris', *Round Table* (Keio University), 5 (1990), 36–42.

Yoon, Hye-joon, 'Ruskin's Gothic', *Journal of English Language and Literature*, 38 (1992), 701–13.